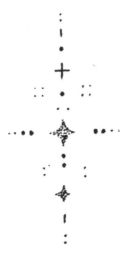

EAT HERE NOW

EAT HERE NOW

A BITE-SIZED GUIDE
TO RITUALIZE YOUR LIFE,
NOURISH YOUR BODY AND
FEED YOUR SPIRIT

BRITTA GUDMUNSON

Eat Here Now: a bite-sized guide to ritualize your life, nourish your body and feed your spirit.

Copyright © 2017 by Britta Gudmunson

The content of this book is for general purposes only. Each person's physical, emotional, and spiritual condition is unique. The instruction in this book is not intended to replace or interrupt the reader's relationship with a physician or other professional. The advice and strategies contained in the book may not be suitable for all readers. Please consult your doctor for matters pertaining to your specific health and diet.

Neither the author, publisher, IIN* nor any of their employees or representatives guarantees the accuracy of information in this book or its usefulness to a particular reader, nor are they responsible for any damage or negative consequence that may result from any treatment, action taken, or inaction by any person reading or following the information in this book.

To contact the publisher or author, visit
www.brittagreenviolet.com
ISBN: 978-0-692-87372-4
Printed in the United States of America

GREEN VIOLET

ACKNOWLEDGEMENTS

Like all fantastic manifestations in my life, this book came to fruition upon seeds of encouragement by my beloved community. Many angels, seen and unseen, contributed their time, energy, input and creative juju into these pages, and I kindly thank you.

Gratitude to the Institute of Integrative Nutrition™ for their provocative and extensive curriculum which inspired the essence of this project, and whose staff and community supported this process from idea to publication. Special thanks to Joshua Rosenthal, creator of IIN™, for initiating such a profound ripple effect.

Gratitude to my beloved community of muses, students, clients, teachers and friends, who were kind enough to contribute their wisdom and guidance. My beloved Benjamin Gould, for your endless support, fantastic namestorming abilities and astounding patience with me. I love you. Patra Arnold and Ishmiel Lounsbury, for holding me in the cradle of your home and welcoming us into your family. There's nowhere else I would rather be.

Gratitude to my fabulous content editor, Danielle Laquer, for your keen eye, your humor, for holding me accountable to complete such a momentous task as publishing a book, and for the reminder to, when in doubt, make it sexy.

Gratitude to my irreplaceable copy editor, Judi Cleghorn, for birthing me into this world and always holding me to the highest standards of writing. If I resisted your teachings as a child, I am beyond grateful now!

Gratitude to all my friends, colleagues, wisdom teachers, sages and heros quoted or referenced in this book: Thich Nat Hahn, His Holiness the Dali Lama, Esther (Abraham) Hicks, Michael Pollan, Angeles Arrien, Tom Malterre, Eddie Ellner and Forest Sterns.

Gratitude to Kris Davidson and Catiflor, for your transcendent artistry; for the cosmic carrot adorning the cover of this book, and for the most delicate and synchronistic of heart chakra tattoos. I am grateful for all the ways in which your medicine infuses my life.

Gratitude to Rosa Penn for your interior layout design and expertise.

And last but certainly not least, thank you to my parents, Rick and Judi, for your love, counsel and faith in my ability to find my way.

My name is I Am.

When you live in the past with it's mistakes and regrets,

It is hard. I am not there. My name is not I Was.

When you live in the future, with it's problems and fears,

It is hard. I am not there. My name is not I Will Be.

When you live in this moment, it is not hard.

I am here.

My name is I Am.

CONTENTS

PREFACE

INTRODUCTIONS

What a joyful thing, for you to pick up this book among the myriad of titles on the topic of food and spiritual practice. I am grateful to have nudged your curiosity to the point of opening these first pages, and I am also thrilled for you! The fact you have explored this book to any extent signals a willingness to begin or continue your own journey into the realm of what I call "holistic nourishment." In simplest terms, this encompasses all the ways we feed ourselves— food, drink, medicine, therapy, relationships, laughter, exercise, meditation, making love, reading a great book, you get the idea— and how they weave together, enfolding us in a blanket of our own making. Holistic nourishment is the way I have come to describe our habits of self-love and self-care. This goes far beyond our daily intake of greens or processed sugar, though indeed those are considerations.

There are many ways we can introduce ourselves. In the interest of full transparency, I will offer two approaches, and let you keep what resonates for your memory bank.

My name is Britta Gudmunson. I am a certified Integrative Nutrition® Health Coach, a Yoga Alliance certified yoga teacher, an essential oil enthusiast, a writer, a musician, an artist, a daughter, a sister, a woman. I assist both men and women to ritualize their lives, to bring the body into alignment with the spirit by cultivating a lasting lifestyle of nourishing practices to keep the mind calm, the body thriving and the heart joyful.

Or,

My name is Britta GreenViolet. I am an open-hearted priestess of love, a servant of the forest, a master manifester, a lover, a music maker, a plant worshiper, a frolicking ecstatic dancer, a mermaid incarnate, a Leo, made of star stuff, luminous with heartfelt gratitude and in awe of life's majesty. I am a student, a leader, a facilitator, a teacher, and a guide, assisting my fellow sisters and brothers in the universal struggle to find harmony and peace in a physical body while navigating this world as a spiritual being.

Kind of amazing, how both these paragraphs describe me. Some of us prefer the factual details, while others opt for the essence. I hope you feel a sense of who I am, because the pages that follow are filled with my personal experiences, lessons and observations, made available to you out of what I deem to be pure necessity.

It is no secret that the United States (and the world at large, really) seriously struggles when it comes to both our physical bodies and our spiritual sanity. My evidence for this lies in the growing percentage of obese Americans, the rise of diseases such as cancer and Alzheimer's, and the civil unrest found pretty much anywhere you look. I found this path of wellness, like many wounded healers, through my own illness and imbalance. And while I have, to quote a favorite Robert Frost poem, "many miles to go before I sleep,"[1] it is extremely satisfying to study that which perplexes me with a courageous heart. For I believe it requires us to have a mightily courageous heart to walk such a path.

COURTED BY CURIOSITY

While I always feel the beginning is an ideal place to start, I wrote this book as a series of essays, grouped into larger categories, all pertaining to the goal of spiritual advancement through practices of physical nourishment. My vision is for this book to be a gift to your home library, placed on a coffee table or bedside table or installed in a reading nook of your own devising, to be enjoyed at your leisure and perused again and again. The idea here is not perfection. I am the first to protest that term and instead rally for the notion of steady practice. I, the author, am with full knowing offering these suggested practices out into the world as I simultaneously work them into my own daily life.

Some concepts may jump out to you as something you've considered many times but never committed to, while others may as well be written in Japanese for your utter unfamiliarity or willingness to take on such a task. Fear not! I invite you to see this collection of practices as a playground, and inevitably we will run to our favorite toy first. This is exactly right. Start where you are comfortable, where you are resonating, where you are most curious.

Some of you may choose to go straight for the practices that freak you out the most, that absolutely repel you, that make you want to hurl this book in the trash (but please, consider recycling or donating it instead). Good for you! As one of my cosmic mentors Abraham Hicks claims, "you can't get it wrong and you'll never get it done." So start anywhere that beckons you, let yourself be courted by your curiosity and guided by intrigue, and go at any pace that feels welcoming. You may read the first chapter and stop there to try out the suggestions found therein, or you might read the entire book through, bookmarking the tidbits that peek your interest and returning to them after you've entertained the entirety of the material.

However you choose to go forth, follow your intuition, follow your gut, and remember that the trick to forming any new practice is consistency. Some experts claim that it takes 21 days to form a new habit. Though this estimate is debatable, give yourself time, exercise patience and, for goodness sakes, be kind to yourself along the way. At the foundation of nourishing ourselves holistically lives a willingness— or rather, an insistence— that we treat ourselves with the same loving kindness with which we would treat our dearest beloved. Laugh at your follies, keep breathing, and know I will be here, believing in you, believing in your ability to expand.

I live in Santa Barbara, California, and work with clients in person as well as remotely. If this work sparks a fire in your heart that requires further kindling, reach out. I am overjoyed to be working with individuals who value their health and happiness like the most precious diamond, because truly, I believe there is no deeper act of humanity we can undertake than our own self-care. If we ourselves are loved, cared for and thriving, then we are fully available to be of service and give our gifts freely to our fellows and our planet. To connect with me, visit my website, brittagreenviolet.com, and we'll embrace the great mystery together...

With an open heart and boundless blessings,

Britta G.

CHAPTER 1
EATING, A SPIRITUAL FRONTIER

YOUR PLATE OF WORSHIP

Welcome to your new spiritual practice.

That plate in front of you? That is your altar, your temple, your prayer rug, your yoga mat, your place of worship.

The popular saying goes, you are what you eat. I propose you are also where you eat, and how you eat. This is to say the very act of eating, besides being absolutely basic and essential to survival, is also deeply symbolic. If you consider yourself a spiritual practitioner of any sort, you have likely discovered the most mundane of details to be the most profound. So it is with food and eating.

The key difference between this spiritual practice and all others lies in the repetition and necessity of taking sustenance into our body. Herein lies the real beauty of this heroic challenge. Should you choose to accept it, this practice will face you head on, day after day, meal after meal, spoonful after spoonful, one bite at a time, for the rest of your days.

Will you be 100% successful? No.

Will you fall again and again into mindless chewing? Probably.

While we must carve out time and practice discipline to show up for meditation, there is hardly a question of whether we will make the effort to show up for at least three meals a day.

Will you savor each flavor and texture as if it were a delicious lover caressing your tongue with titillating, spicy, honey-sweet sensation? Highly doubtful.

And yet, is this an idea worth pursuing? Unequivocally, yes.

ON THE WORD "PRACTICE"

There is a very good reason why our spiritual endeavors are called practices.

Merriam-Webster's defines practice, as:

a. to carry out, apply (practice what you preach)

b. to do or perform often, customarily, or habitually (practice politeness)

c. to be professionally engaged in (practice medicine)

d. to perform or work at repeatedly so as to become proficient (practice the act)

e. to train by repeated exercises (practice pupils in penmanship)

Practice implies that we show up, time and time again, despite the results. Sure, as some forms of the definition suggest, we hope that eventually, we will improve. Yet practice does not necessarily correlate to the notion of results; they are two separate topics. At some point, someone popularized the phrase *practice makes perfect*. This is utter nonsense that begs to be addressed, because as a population we have wholeheartedly bought into the idea that if we just show up enough, we will reach perfection. And once we summit the mountain, I guess we can just go home!

The truth is this: perfection is a fallacy. It is as fantastical and imaginary as glittering rainbow-striped winged unicorns carrying us to and from our job at the office every day.

Perfection is a myth requiring impolite deconstruction. I happily take a go at it by sharing the wisdom of the illustrious San Francisco-based illustrator Forest Sterns, an exquisitely talented friend of mine, who offers this alternative: "practice makes practice." Perhaps this feels deflating in comparison. Good. What is deflating is our ego, so let that balloon be crushed by gravity and celebrate the freedom of all that imprisoned oxygen. When we strive for perfection, we focus on end results, placing our attention upon outcome and displacing our attention from the present moment. Furthermore, we place that ideal outcome in a kingdom so far away it actually doesn't exist, and then we feel crushed beyond measure when we never reach it. Setting ourselves up for failure and heartache appears to be a cultural trait, and certainly a learned one. Instead, what would it feel like to focus upon the practice itself? What if our 'goal' was to be here now, practicing, mindful, present in our focus, one action at a time? That seems attainable, yes? It is, of course, up to you which path you will walk. Option A: a goal-oriented fantasy of perfection. Option B: a path-oriented, present-minded practice.

I recommend the option that feels better to you, because here is the secret to success: it is all about the way you feel, folks.

VOTE WITH YOUR SPOON

Food holds an obvious seat at our grand table of requirements. Given a place of honor and reverence, we bow down to our plate and utensils (be it fork, spoon, chopsticks or fingers) and acknowledge heartily that we could not survive without feeding ourselves. Unfortunately, as is often the case with us humans, the pendulum swings to both extremes, and we swing right along. Our reverence becomes a meal we take for granted. We forget the utter miracle of not only the edible delights we consume, but the incredible event occurring inside our mouth and digestive tract that transform our nourishment into energy and vitality. When we lose sight of this commonplace evidence of the divine, trouble ensues. Obesity, disease, negative body image, eating disorders, depression, and a general lack of presence all point like blinking neon signs to a major oversight. When we rush through a meal or feed ourselves "edible food-like

> Food is our most direct bridge between the external and the internal, giving us an infinite supply of opportune moments to reflect and connect with the world outside and the world inside.

substances" (a term coined by master food journalist Michael Pollan), we miss a vital and loving opportunity for connection to ourselves, our source, our planet. The widespread display of deeply unhealthy habits signals a culture lost in the dark.

I choose this practice because when I appreciate my food, I appreciate myself and the planet I inhabit. Just as we vote with our dollars, we also vote with our actions. I vote that we, as a society, take back the ancient tradition of holistic nourishment that is our birthright, passed down to us by a long lineage of ancestors known and unknown. I vote to carry the torch to the best of my ability and take steps, one at a time, towards a world humbled by the gift of life. To be emphatically grateful for the splendiferous bounty at our fingertips. I vote to care for our planet Earth with tender reverence and full awareness that she is our mother, and the master of our fate as a species.

Thus, I vote with my fork, knife and spoon. I choose to take this practice on with an open heart and an open mind.

Would you like to join me?

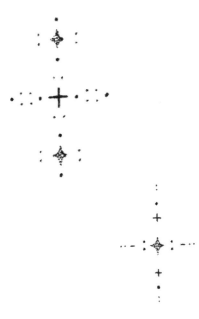

CHAPTER 2
A LITTLE TASTE

The word "prayer" delivers a religious aftertaste for many people, but I feel a personal mission to reclaim such words from their dogmatic encapsulation. So when I submit the proposal that we make our meal into a prayer, I mean simply to allow this mundane action to humble us. It could be argued that food is godliness; after all, we could not be without our nourishment, and that nourishment is a direct manifestation of creation (whatever that means to you).

This is all to say that the act of eating a meal is worth our reverence and even our worship, so let us discuss the scene. To honor the food we eat, there are some simple offerings that, when made, become a gesture of gratitude and attention.

First, where do you cook? I'm going to assume you cook in a kitchen like most folks. Take a look around your kitchen. Is it clean? Organized? Tidy? Are the countertops cluttered? How about the state of your drawers, cupboards, pantry and refrigerator? Do you love, or loath, your knife collection? Whether our first response to these inquiries is cringing or glowing, the point is to notice the environment in which we prepare our nourishment.

Now (what other time is there?) would be an opportune time to make any adjustments to your cooking space. Take note of which aspects need an upgrade. Material matters! When in doubt, steel, ceramic or glass are always preferable over plastic, aluminum or Teflon. Keep a running list of items you'd like to acquire, stored in your wallet or on your phone, so you have it handy when you stroll by the antique store or find yourself at a yard sale or next door to an Ikea.

Here is a simple list of kitchen basics to consider:

- Cutting boards

- Utensils (cooking, eating, serving)

- Pots & pans (beware of Teflon!)

- Colanders & steamers

- Measuring cups & spoons

- Knives & a method for sharpening them (or find a local place to get them sharpened)

- Appliances (food processor, blender, juicer, etc)

- Kitchen tools (shredder, peeler, citrus press, can opener, etc)

- Glass jars and food storage containers

Next, perhaps designate a regular cleaning schedule. Half an hour once a week, on the same day and time, treated just like a shift at your job. Be punctual and devote yourself to the task with a joyful heart. Put on some music, and while you're at it, install some speakers in your kitchen space so you have the option of listening to music. While musical tastes, of course, vary, may I recommend something peaceful?

Soothe yourself while you are in your kitchen. There are plenty of perfect moments to rock out; while handling scalding pots and sharp knives is not one of them.

Many organizing experts offer free tips and tricks online. Take advantage and put these bits of genius to use. For instance, using labeled jars in your pantry to hold your grains, legumes, teas and spices is a brilliant way to clean up your space and makes your ingredients easy to find. Simultaneously, you will develop environmentally sustainable awareness. Jars are reusable, refillable, recyclable, multi-purpose, and can even be taken to the grocery store with you and used in lieu of plastic bags. We shall revisit this topic later...

The next question is where do you eat? Likely (hopefully), you eat at a table. This would be an appropriate moment to point out the places where, barring exceptional circumstances, I do not recommend consuming a meal. This includes standing on your feet anywhere, walking or driving. As the Vietnamese mindfulness guru Thich Nat Hahn so eloquently requests, "please sit when you eat."⁵

Designate one spot in your home where you will, more often than not, consume your meals. A dining table, perhaps? This table should be kept free from clutter and wiped down after each sitting, so that you always have a clean slate upon which to worship your edibles. Find comfortable chairs so your rump is welcomed with each meeting at your dining table.

From here, your creative and personal aesthetic inclinations will take over. Let your own style define your table, and be adventurous. I personally indulge in an array of multicolored and textured placemats and napkins. (No, they do not have to match.) Find a set of utensils and chopsticks that you absolutely die over, because life is fleeting and impermanent, so why not eat with things you adore? Same idea for glasses, mugs, plates and bowls. No need to go crazy with a huge collection, but select an amount of tableware that suits your normal household flow of inhabitants and guests and is suited to the type of cuisine normally consumed.

Set the mood, light some candles, entice yourself in preparation for the ultimate and most basic of indulgences. It doesn't need to be ornate.

> **Before eating, the simple act of setting the table is important — kind of like foreplay.**

You could find yourself eating cross legged on the floor, a plate in your lap, using your fingers (indeed, the majority of human beings eat in a similar manner). Or, make an intricate spread with silk linens and crystal goblets on a carved mahogany table, if you must. Either way, this preparatory phase of creating a sacred space in which to enjoy your meal is key.

THREE BREATHS

This practice, like all true spiritual practices, begins with a deep, slow breath.

As a yoga teacher, I quickly discovered that no matter what type of class I was offering, the first place to begin was breath. Notice your breathing. Listen to the sound it creates. Feel the expansion of the ribs, the shifting of the shoulders, the inflation of the belly, the fullness of the heartspace. Lengthen the inhale, then match that length with your exhale. Breathe in and out through the nostrils— this breath, as opposed to mouth breathing, is hailed as the absolute best, swiftest and most efficient way to calm the nervous system.

After sitting down at the table and before you even touch your utensils, stop and take three deep rounds of breath. If you find yourself hurried and impatient to dig into the mound of goodness in front of you, all the better reason to stop and appreciate the moment. This is a perfect time to set an intention of mindful eating for the meal. I like three deep breaths rather than one. This creates an opportunity as well to reflect on the very state of your nervous system. How are you feeling at this particular moment in time? What is the state of your heart? How active is your mind? How hungry is your belly? What kind of food does it actually want? When we practice mindfulness, we are emptying the

With one breath, there is a real possibility of rushing through it, the meal before you dangling in front of your nose like the carrot in front of the horse. Savor three breaths to step willingly into the practice.

mind to a certain degree, orienting our headspace to that which resides in the present moment. If concerns, judgments, fantasies, anxieties or plotting thoughts fill the landscape of our inner vision, we cannot clearly see the delectable morsels in front of us. Your breath is your best bet and your very best tool to access the here and now.

GRACIAS, MADRE

Another morsel of this endeavor resides in the invitation to give thanks. If you are like me, you may not have been raised by a family that 'says grace' before each meal. In fact, the very picture of a 'good' family, sitting around a tidy table, holding hands and offering a blessing is rather antiquated when viewed through societal lenses. Like many rituals in our modern-day living, we have the opportunity to redefine these mini-ceremonies and create authentic gesture from an open heart.

Truthfully, there is much to be grateful for; from the food on our plate, to the bodies sitting here at the table, to all the cosmic elements that alchemically combined in a perfectly stewed concoction, giving rise to the bread of our existence. I could write an entirely separate book simply listing reasons to be grateful at the supper table! The point is, here is a chance to begin creating your own living, breathing connection to the inner and outer world, and to the food that is about to nurture you.

If you dine alone, try simply gazing at your plate as you would gaze upon a dear beloved. Perhaps you might try holding your palms over or around the nourishment, beaming superpower blessings through your skin and onto your plate. This food is about to embark on a journey into you, after all, so you may as well do your best to imbibe it with every ounce of good juju you can muster. A gesture of prayer (also known as *Anjali mudra* or namaste hands) is certainly appropriate. I also enjoy placing one hand over my belly and the other hand over my heart. This is a fine place for our hands during our three deep breaths as well, to fully embody the physical spaces where breath resides.

If you dine among others, be they beloveds or strangers, you have two obvious options. You can either take a few quiet moments to yourself to offer your blessings and gratitude, or you can invite those around you to participate. Quaint though it may seem, I do enjoy taking hands and uniting with others in this age-old tradition. Allow this experience to be enjoyable, interesting, full of curiosity.

If it feels awkward, great. Lean into it.

Moments of uncertainty are a wonderful indicator that we are stretching and growing beyond our previous capacity. Most importantly, know this: there is no wrong way to offer thanks. Here is a chance to usher in the sacred, in any way that feels honestly expressed. It may be subtle or extremely woo-woo. Sing a song, hum a note, take turns offering a word for what each feels grateful for today. Do it your way, or if you're shy, perhaps invite someone bolder to lead the group. It need not be lengthy (better if it's not) and there is certainly no reason for it to be dull! My dear brother Leif Cederbloom offers this profound and humble chant before a meal…

Yuuuuuuuuuuuuuuummmmmmmmmmmmmmmmmmmmmmmmm.

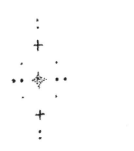
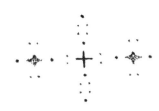

CHAPTER 3
DIGGING IN

HABIT OF HYDRATION

Water is the true medicine, the original solution, and the best prescription. Its necessity cannot be overstated, and the list of common ailments stemming from dehydration is extensive. Headaches, hangovers, cravings, exhaustion, constipation, blemished skin; these imbalances, plus many more, are symptoms of a parched system, and while there may be other factors involved, the truth is that water is our very best friend.

So why is it so difficult to drink enough of it?

Cultivating a habit of hydration, like everything else in this book, is a practice. It requires vigilance, mindfulness, attentiveness, and our willingness to once again become a disciple unto ourselves, listening keenly for the tiny whispers that beg for the lifeblood before our situation becomes dire.

I see our remoteness from water as a clear reflection of our indifference to nature. The layers of this predicament are constantly unfolding and multiplying and tightening in upon themselves, like a genetically modified artichoke, until the heart of the truth is so tightly tucked away out of sight that we only have an inkling of its existence. We remember what it is to feel good, to feel hydrated and moisturized. But, my, oh my, it feels like such work to get there through all those layers. Let us begin to deconstruct this conundrum, plucking one armored petal at a time, until all that remains is the moist, tantalizing molecule upon which our very lives depend.

Here, I will list some commonly offered excuses and myths around the difficulty of drinking enough water, and then I will offer some simple steps to correct the course and get you on the path to healthy hydration.

Dehydration Excuse #1: Water tastes bland/I don't like the taste.

Water tastes bland if you are accustomed to drinking liquids and consuming foods filled with sugar on a regular basis. I hope it will be obvious that this is not only problematic, but avoidable and also correctable. If you were raised on soda pop and orange juice and reach for one of those so-called 'energy drinks' when you are tired or thirsty, devote yourself to this area. It is never too late to begin new habits, regardless of that *old dog* slogan. Besides, using this excuse is as good as throwing in the towel. You must be willing to stop what you are doing, to carry a water bottle around with you even when it is not fashionable; to recognize the fundamental nature of this aqueous essence and make sacrifices to take it into your body.

The simple truth is that if you want to be your healthiest self, you must drink plenty of water every single day of your life.

Drinking water is a prerequisite of health, so get into it.

Dehydration Excuse #2: Water makes me urinate frequently, which is annoying.

You know how smokers take smoke breaks throughout their day? They are devoted (and yes, addicted) to their habit, and they make time for it. I am not saying this is a wise habit to cultivate, but it is an interesting comparison I've noted over time. Many folks are reluctant to take more water into their bodies because, yes, you will need to empty your bladder more often. Hey, reader! This is a good thing!

When we release waste, be it solid or liquid, we are detoxifying our system. Water is not only hydrating for every cell in your physical form, it functions the same way as flushing a clog in your drainage pipe. We cleanse our bodies when we urinate often, and though it is possible to overhydrate, most of us will seldom to never get

The complaint of needing to use the bathroom too often is another symptom of our perfectionistic, overworking cultural mentality, where we are attached to productivity but fail to realize that many of our daily habits actually destroy our potential effectiveness.

that far. In addition, I invite you to look at those bodily demands as an epic excuse to get up, walk away from your desk and take a mini break!

We are far more productive when we allow ourselves short breaks, stretch our limbs and get our blood flowing a bit. Allow yourself to contemplate the possibility that using the restroom more often is a magical portal into a more vibrant state of being where, despite all your preconceived notions, your productivity, focus and creative potential will burst forth exponentially in a blinding, shimmering rainbow of splendor.

Dehydration Excuse #3: I get my water by drinking tea, coffee and/or sparkling water.

If these are common thoughts in your brain, please brace yourself as I skewer the bubble of misconception in which you are floating. To be clear, none of these substances are evil, and in fact, they are all wonderful elixirs containing their own healing properties. When used in moderation, that is. However, these beverages are not a replacement for water by any stretch of the imagination.

Water is not only beneficial for us because it is hydrating; it is also alkalizing and cleansing for our gut, organs and intestines, and benefits nearly all of our bodily systems from hair and nail growth to skin health and blood pressure.

Both coffee and sparkling water are extremely acidic, which can throw off the pH balance of our system if consumed too heavily. Coffee is also known to be quite dehydrating, which makes it a pretty poor choice as the first beverage consumed upon waking up each morning. Tea is actually a great choice as a daily beverage, but we must also look at caffeine content, additives in the tea itself, whether it is organic or grown with pesticides, and any sweetener or creamers you might add. These additional factors affect your whole system and cannot be overlooked, and also apply to how you take your coffee. One cup of joe each morning on its own may not necessarily be a bad thing, but if you throw in some sugar and cream, you need to be honest about what is seeping into your system.

Hydration Suggestion #1: The First Thing

When you wake up in the morning, I invite you to make water your very first priority. Drink one quart of it. Fill a jar or glass before you go to sleep at night and challenge yourself to drink the entire thing before you even get out of bed the next morning. See it as a delicious excuse to lounge in bed another ten minutes. If you live in a cold climate, you may want to fill your quart with warm water— avoid making it so hot you cannot easily drink it down. The idea here is not to slowly sip on this quart for an hour or two, but to consume it swiftly, kicking your daily hydration into high gear, first thing. Watch how this amazingly simple tip assists you to wake up, move your bowels with more ease and feel more energy throughout your day.

Hydration Suggestion #2: Ritualize It

Just as we've discussed with our food, here is another opportunity to alchemize the mundane into the sacred. Sure, you could see that glass of clear liquid as plain, boring ol' water. Or, you could take the vessel lovingly into your hands, close your eyes, and take several breaths, calling in the awareness of the immense gift you hold. You could imagine your body as the mostly liquid temple it actually is. Then you could imagine planet earth, 71% of whose surface is covered in water; then you could draw a link, a golden thread, between yourself and your mother planet, imagining the waters swirling inside you and in the great oceans, rivers, creeks, lakes and streams, allowing yourself and the planet to merge, seeing yourself as one with this world to which you inherently belong. You could give silent thanks to the water for offering itself to you. You could send prayers to this water in your hands, asking it to nourish you and soothe your ills; and you could send prayers to all the waters of this world; the polluted oceans, the oil-soaked shores, the dammed rivers, and to all the wildlife living in those toxic waters who depend on this life-giving element, just like you and I. You could offer your apologies for the ignorance with which we have treated our sacred waters. You could ask forgiveness. And then, you could slowly, deliberately, intentionally, lovingly, take a drink.

Hydration Suggestion #3: Jazz It Up

If, after all that woo, you still find water tasteless and dull but at least recognize its vital role, try adding some fresh berries, cucumbers, or citrus, bestowing your water with not only flavor but also additional nutrients. Make a big jug or decanter in the morning, then sip on it throughout the day. Fresh herbs such as rosemary, basil and mint are also delicious and offer their own medicinal properties. Find flavor combinations that make you crave your water!

I also love to use high quality, therapeutic grade essential oils in my glass or metal water bottle. Lemon, peppermint, wild orange, grapefruit, the list goes on and like adding herbs, you not only delight in the taste but receive the gifts of their therapeutic benefit (see chapter 5 for more on high quality essential oils).

Hydration Suggestion #4: Go Herbal

If you are a tried and true tea drinker like yours truly (and many, many citizens of this world), select non-caffeine herbal teas as often as possible. Visit your local herb store or natural foods market and get friendly with the bulk section. Avoid additives and buy organic whenever possible. Blending your own herbs is a chance to get into your kitchen and be an inventor. I had a friend who, on one trip to the store, bought a small bag of each herb that started with the letter 'L', then brought them home and brewed up a Licorice Lemongrass Lavender elixir that was truly lovely. Buying herbs in bulk also allows you to build your own apothecary, from which you can brew an infinite number of healing concoctions for any ailment plaguing you. There are countless books on herbs to educate you on a variety of commonly used plants and their therapeutic properties.

Hydration Suggestion #5: Adjust The Temperature

As someone who has spent three decades in the seasonal, climate temperatures of the Pacific Northwest corner of America, I have found it all too easy to become dehydrated in the colder, winter months. Why? Because drinking water is not very appealing from underneath layers of cashmere sweaters, down jackets and wool socks. When we are cold, we want tea, we want hot cocoa, we want coffee! So although we aren't losing as much water through perspiration compared with the warmer months, it can be difficult to drink enough for proper hydration. Furthermore, some of us may also be more likely to have an extra glass of wine or warming nip of whiskey in the darker days of the year, which can easily turn into a headache come morning simply from a lack of water in our bodies. Thankfully, there is a very simple solution to this conundrum. Warm it up! Do not let the weather or the season or your Doshic constitution be an excuse for dehydration.

Speaking of Doshas, it is also worth mentioning that most restaurants offer their patrons ice water by default. I myself prefer not to drink much water with my meal at all, a digestion tip offered by the ancient system of Ayurveda, which claims that water dilutes our stomach acids and therefore slows the GI tract from doing its job. Moreover, ice water is (obviously) cooling, which also counteracts our so-called digestive fire. If either of these ideas resonate with you, simply decline being served water at a restaurant, or request a glass of water with no ice.

Your server will be happy to accommodate you, and you'll save some additional resources from being poured down the drain untouched.

As a final recommendation on this topic, if you'd like to experiment with offering extra support to your gut by not drinking water with your meals, I recommend making sure you are well hydrated beforehand so you do not become parched mid meal! About an hour prior to a meal, drink a big glass of water. Give yourself at least 30 minutes without water before digging into your next delicious plateful of awesome.

Suggestion #6: Eat Hydrating Foods

In addition to all those concepts, we can also support a habit of hydration by looking at the foods we are eating, taking extra care to limit our salt intake and eat more fruits and veggies. Fruits like watermelon, oranges, grapefruits and melons all have very high water content, as do vegetables like cucumber, celery, tomatoes, bell peppers and romaine lettuce. As stated above, there are always multiple factors to consider here, like sugar and fiber content. While watermelon is 90% water, one serving also contains 17g of sugar. Considering our daily recommended maximum sugar intake is around 25 grams for women and 36 grams for men,[7] that doesn't give us much wiggle room after that slice of melon goes down. Those numbers reflect the amount of 'added sugar' versus natural sugar, which is an important distinction to understand. But, in truth, our body metabolizes both kinds of sugar the same once they reach our gut. Though fruit breaks down more slowly due to the added factors of fiber and other nutrients, both natural and added sugars are transformed into glucose and fructose and can have negative effects in our body.[8]

Choose your hydration wisely and diversify those choices. Water in its purest form is always your safest bet.

EAT HERE NOW

While it is tempting to add stimulating elements to our dining table like condiments to a burger (mmmm, burger...), I invite you to reconsider your motives.

If our practice is to be present with our food, what happens to our mind when we add in elements of media? iPhones, laptops, magazines and books are often fixtures beside our plate, resulting in the task of splitting our attention. It is my experience that while we believe we humans are wonderfully efficient multi-taskers, we are kidding ourselves to the utmost degree. If we want to do anything with 100% mindfulness, it is a simple equation that we must devote 100% of our attention, and 100% of our intention, to the task at hand.

Quite simply, removing your media from your eating experience leaves you with just the food and yourself. Though many of us are averse to imposing rules in our lives (a perpetual backlash of teenage adolescence, perhaps?), I recommend installing this basic rule: no media during meals. Leave these important tokens of your day behind as you sit with your nourishment. They will still be there after you finish. If you are a parent, lead by example and enforce this rule with your children. Especially these days, the youth of America are overly inundated with digital data and have built expectation around having literally the world at their fingertips 24/7. But come on. We can do this, people!

We can survive for 30 minutes without our smartphones while we eat our food. The result is a bigger opening for gratitude and presence, which can teach us more by far than the World Wide Web ever could.

If you eat with company, first of all what a blessing to be surrounded by loved ones and fellows. Second of all, consider how even this affects your attention towards your food. Carried away in enthralling or even mundane conversation, we can completely miss the fact that we are picking up a utensil, transporting food to our mouth, chewing, and swallowing. How common is it that at the end of the meal, we hardly recall the actual taste and texture in our mouth?

I'm not suggesting any rules here, but rather curiosity. The culture of macrobiotics teaches to chew each bite so thoroughly that any conversation is virtually impossible. One idea would be to experiment with this idea. Try to not speak with food in your mouth. Some of you may be saying, yeah, duh! But I say it again, and a bit more directly this time.

Please do not speak while you have food in your mouth.

Chew and swallow each bite before conversing. If you have something important to say, then put your utensil down, take a deep breath and let yourself speak. Your food can wait. Certainly, you can enjoy a wonderful meal with friends in this way; taking turns speaking while the other is chewing and swallowing. But let me break this down a bit further in clarifying that this endeavor entails chewing and listening at the same time. Some of you may think, oh piece of cake, I do that all the time! But are you really listening? Can you truly divide your attention equally between attentively, actively listening to your dining mates, and fully enjoying each bite as it is tasted, chewed, and digested? Perhaps you can. I encourage you to give it a real try, and be honest with yourself about the outcome in regards to the quality of your mindfulness. I might go further and ask if you prefer being listened to with 50% of your friend's attention, or 100% of your friend's attention? The art of listening is another can of beans all together. Perhaps we'll pry off it's lid now.

THE ART OF LISTENING

The act of listening may not exactly be relevant to eating in particular (unless you are munching on some crunchy blue corn tortilla chips, a crisp Braeburn apple or a vibrantly verdant stick of celery...), but it sure is relevant to the practice of mindfulness. Very, very relevant.

The honorable Ralph Waldo Emerson wisely offered, "There is a difference between truly listening and waiting for your turn to talk." In other words, the art of listening means opening ourselves to receive and taking in each word or sound fully. Emerson's quote calls to my mind the difference between bartering and gifting. To barter is to offer goods in exchange for receiving goods; in other words, there is expectation involved. An eye for an eye, if you will. To gift is to offer goods to another with no expectation of receiving anything in return.

On parallel ground is the act of listening. To truly listen to another human being, or to the sounds of the forest or the rolling life of the ocean or the hum of the city, is a gift to us. We open ourselves and we receive, and that is the point. Should we find ourselves judging what we hear, or offering feedback, or slinging advice, we have forced ourselves upon an issue that does not require and did not ask for our response. It is often referred to as the "art" of listening because this practice is indeed a skill we must develop and practice again and again in order to master. It is worth doing. Because to be the speaker when someone is fully inhabiting their presence and listening to us with all their being is the most wonderful gift our friends can give us. The simple act of being heard is deeply healing. That is why it is worth doing. It is this quality of mindfulness that I speak of in this book. It is this quality of mindfulness that I hope to bring to each crumb of divinity that enters my being. And it is a practice.

This same concept of honorable listening can be applied to listening to our body. I find that when I force myself into the driver's seat, insisting that I (my mind) know best, that is when I push myself beyond my own reasonable limits. In all its innate wisdom, our bodies sound those piercing alarm bells to alert us when our immune system is teetering on the edge of illness, or the nervous system dangerous

If we are still, and paying attention, we can plainly hear the messages that we are satiated, that we are thirsty, that we are exhausted.

careening into the abyss of overwhelm. Just as I can practice listening to my beloved or my mother by quietly holding space and taking in their words without judgment, so I can practice listening to my body in the same manner— allowing whatever information arises to surface without constraint or denial, then handling the situation accordingly, with as much tender loving care as I would with someone other than myself.

If your sweetheart approached you with a worry cast over their face and said, "Babe, I so beat that I am afraid of even handling a kitchen knife," would you respond by reminding them it is their night to cook and insisting they get to work? Offer them a cup of espresso? Or might you encourage them to lay down for a 20-minute nap, or even go to bed early? There is a strange truth that exists for most of us wherein we treat ourselves with a surprising amount of harsh malice in comparison to how we treat our loved ones. Why on earth do we feel this is justifiable? We are human beings, and our bodies require care and maintenance to function optimally. If you find yourself giving more weight to the needs of others than your own, and if you find yourself squashing the seemingly meager requests for rest, movement, nourishment or boundaries arising from your own body, take heed. These bodies of ours are far from invincible.

Often, it seems the focus for living a spiritual life falls on transcending the physical form, but a pivotal piece of a spiritual being having a human experience is to accept this 'human experience' as a classroom where deeply meaningful teachings transpire.

If you can believe it is no accident you are here on earth, right now, in this exact incarnation of the body you currently inhabit, then you are already living a spiritual life. The next step is to accept the mantel of the caretaker, and to take this job seriously. The better we can care for ourselves from a young age, learning to not only hear our body's needs but to heed the call, the more joyful and pleasurable our life shall be. While it is true we are vastly more than what is here physically, in flesh, bone and sinew, what we are seeking as spiritual practitioners is balance between the physical and the metaphysical. Let us not be so attached to our body that we live in terror of its inevitable passing, but remain present while we still exist in this form and caretake our vessel with gratitude and loving devotion.

MASTICATION MEDITATION

The best tool I have found thus far in the practice of mindful eating is the one I am about to offer. This is in no way an original idea I came up with, but rather a tenant of mindful eating taught by the Zen Buddhist mindfulness tradition from time immemorial. Beware: it is profoundly simple and yet eternally challenging.

I call it the Mastication Meditation. It goes like this.

Lift food to lips.
Open mouth.
Insert food into mouth.
Close mouth.
Put down utensil.
Chew.

Keep chewing, and (this part is crucial!) do not pick up your utensil again until you have completely chewed and swallowed your previous bite. I do not suggest any particular number of chews and in fact the idea of counting rather repels me. Chew each bite thoroughly. A friend of mine shared a tidbit of eastern medicinal wisdom that goes something like, "chew your liquids and drink your solids." In other words, pulverize everything that comes into your mouth as if your life depended upon it. Because, in fact, it very well might.

Many are the reasons to adopt a hearty chewing practice. Here are several for you to, well, chew on.

1. Chewing reduces choking.

Again, perhaps this is rather obvious. However, in our daily haste that is so common, if we are not giving each bite the attention it deserves, and if we happen to be in a rush or thinking about our to-do list or occupying our brain with the millions of other competing thoughts, we have likely swallowed food before it is adequately processed. Besides being outright dangerous and life-threatening, this means more work for your digestive system, which means less energy for the rest of your body. Which brings me to...

2. Chewing increases energy.

If the body is not overwhelmed by the process of digestion, you'll have more energy for all the other impressive things you want to do with your life. The human body is the true monarch of multi-tasking. But even it has limits. By design, our blood flows where it is needed most in that moment, dictated by many factors including our nervous and digestive systems. Chewing your food thoroughly inherently entails a slower eating experience, which supports the rest & digest function of your nervous system. By allowing yourself time and space to process your food before it even begins its downward trajectory, you make the gut's job a bit easier. Digestion is hard work. Take it easy on yourself and give your body the best opportunity to focus on the task at hand so you can move on to other matters. It might also help to stop eating when you're full. See #5.

3. Chewing releases enzymes in your mouth that aid with digestion.

Our saliva contains amylase, an enzyme that is released only when you chew, that greatly assists in beginning the process of digestion. While amylase works to break down primarily starches and carbohydrates, other enzymes such as lipase and pepsin focus their processing powers on fats and proteins, respectively. Chewing your food thoroughly into tiny itsy bits also ensures that each molecule is coated in these enzymes as they travel down into your gut. Furthermore, the same can be said about food once it reaches your gut and gets coated with those digestive juices.

4. Chewing releases nutrients.

When we effectively break down our food, we allow all the nutrients to release and assimilate more quickly. For example, the digestive enzymes in our saliva break down fats and turn starches into simple sugars, and longer chewing has been shown to increase the amount of protein our bodies can absorb from our food and put it to use building muscle. Chewing also makes certain vitamins and minerals more available for absorption, particularly from uncooked fruits and vegetables.

In the words of Dr. Joseph Mercola, "Chewing breaks your food down from large particles into smaller particles that are more easily digested. This also makes it easier for your intestines to absorb nutrients and energy from the food particles as they pass through, while also preventing improperly digested food from entering your blood and causing a wide range of adverse effects to your health."[10]

If you're wondering what "adverse effects" refers to, allow me to introduce you to the concept of Leaky Gut Syndrome and the link between autoimmune disorders and digestion. Leaky Gut, or increased gut permeability, is technically a pseudomedical diagnosis[11] not widely recognized by the world of western medicine. More commonly diagnosed and treated by nutritionists and alternative or functional medicine practitioners, Leaky Gut Syndrome is when the lining of the gut, which is already somewhat permeable to allow nutrients through, becomes penetrated by larger particles, leading to nutritional malabsorption, as well as the immune system beginning to identify the larger (often undigested food) particles as invaders (ie, mistaking them for bacteria or viral molecules), and launches an attack, ultimately creating fertile grounds for autoimmune dysfunction.[12]

5. Chewing gives your brain time to catch up with your belly.

When we take the time to fully chew each bite, we are much less likely to overeat to the point of being uncomfortably full, because we will notice when our belly is satiated. The longer we chew, the further we prolong our meal. This is a beautiful bonus not only because we have more time to savor each bite and moment with ourselves and our dining companions, but also because the simple act of mindful chewing assists us in effortless weight maintenance.

It takes roughly 20 minutes for brain and belly to communicate the signal of satiety. If you struggle with feeling overweight, a practice of mindful chewing is an absolute necessity. Diets as a lasting solution to weight loss are as mythical as Zeus and the gods of Mount Olympus crashing your next dinner party. A balanced, holistic, mindful approach to our food is the yellow brick road leading the way to a healthy, vibrant, thriving body.

To sum this up for you in the simplest terms:

Chew more = Eat less = Better digestion = More energy = Happy gut = Happy You.

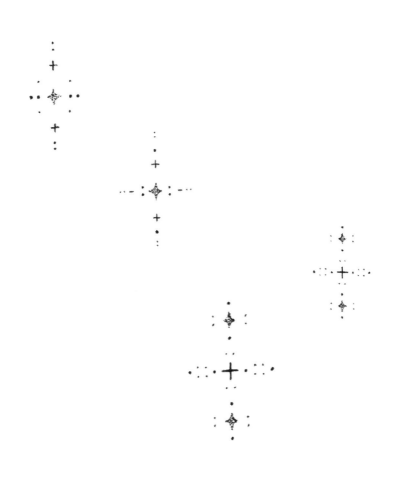

CHAPTER 4
EASY DOES IT

If we are going to choose to see our plate as our place of worship, it is worth considering how we hold ourselves at the table. We've made the effort to breathe deeply and give thanks, and often it is at this point that we lose our cool completely. In our state of hunger, which may range from peckish to ravenous, instead of slowly dipping into the tasty morsels in front of us, we dive face-first in a mad rush to satiate ourselves. This often results in what can only be described as hunchback posture. I doubt I need to really explain, as you're probably receiving a pretty clear visual of what I'm describing... Those in this category have a habit of bending deeply forward in the thoracic spine, literally hunching over the table, cervical spine drooping downwards, face arching towards the plate, one or both arms on the table holding utensils.

If you are unsure whether this describes you or not, here's a polite invitation for a rude awakening. Get your smartphone out and go to the video setting. If you've got an app for taking time lapse video, use it (iPhone 6 models have a time lapse setting built right into the video camera options). Set your camera up to film yourself from a profile view while you sit at your table. Then, to the very best of your ability, forget about the camera and go about nourishing yourself as you normally would. Make your best effort to not change anything from your normal routine because this is strictly for your own research, and it would behoove you to get the most honest results possible. Film yourself for an entire meal, then retrieve your camera, sit back and watch the show. Take a deep breath and observe yourself with an objective lens over your eyes. Allow your attention to rest not on that piece of hair misbehaving or that unflattering shadow under your chin, but rather strictly noticing the shape and alignment of your spine and your general posture while you eat.

If, in your experiment, you discover some disturbing results, fret not. It's not too late for you to straighten yourself out! The most important factor in bringing our spine upright during our meals is our breath. We discussed the importance of taking at least three deep breaths before beginning our meals, and I now insert a further suggestion. Notice your breathing in between bites, and allow that spaciousness created by the mindful chewing exercise to be an opportunity to unfurl your spine and allow the energy to flow from crown to tailbone. We must inevitably lean forward slightly to bring our utensils to our lips, otherwise we'd be dropping food into our lap. Not so elegant. Almost like a dance, let yourself lean forward to take a bite. Then as you place your utensils down, allowing time for the mastication meditation, rise back up, fair friend, and take a breath to elongate yourself vertical once more. This can be a beautiful ebb and flow. Seated table yoga, you might call it.

Just as in certain asana poses we elongate on the inhale and then deepen the stretch on the exhale, visualize each bite as an opportunity to move towards and away from your plate.

The true indicator of how well you will be able to control this is your patience. If you wait to eat until you feel voracious, you will find it more difficult to practice any measure of serenity while you take your meal. So another factor here is to make an effort to eat your meals before you are starving. Any true spiritual practice is grounded in patience. Eating is no exception. When we slow ourselves down, we open ourselves up to receiving numerous benefits. We have more time and space to take deep pleasure in the flavors of our food. We give our gut a better chance to fully digest each bite, and slowing ourselves down while we chew means we will likely eat less since we will realize we are full much sooner than if we were shoveling bites down our throat. All the while, your back will thank you, as the muscles won't need to work so hard and your vertebrae will be able to stack upon each other as they are meant to. When we stack our bones properly, our muscles don't need to work so hard to hold us up. This ease in our front and back body contributes not only to a calm state of mind while we feed ourselves, but also activates the rest and digest mechanism that defines our parasympathetic nervous system.

REST & DIGEST

One of the most important concepts I've discovered to maintaining my physical and emotional wellbeing is the dramatic interplay taking place constantly in the autonomic nervous system. I first really began to tune into the role of the nervous system in my 200-hour yoga teaching training. This understanding deepened through my work with essential oils, which led me to study how aromatherapy affects the brain and extends outward into physiological responses. The simplified breakdown goes like this: our autonomic nervous system has two branches, the sympathetic and the parasympathetic. We are all intimately familiar with both aspects of the nervous system, even if we don't recognize them by their scientific names. What might ring a more familiar bell are the terms "fight or flight" and "rest and digest."

Fight or flight is the sympathetic nervous system. It exists to protect us, activating when there are threats in our environment. Stress is a key ingredient in this equation, and while we have formulated a complex relationship with that word which usually carries with it a negative connotation, its ultimate purpose is benevolent.

Imagine, for example, you are walking along a country road, blissful in the dappled sunlight streaming through a canopy of oak trees, and suddenly you hear a low, menacing growl. Immediately, tension floods your entire being. Turning around to locate the source of the noise which you instinctually recognize as a threat, you see the jaw-dropping, muscular, golden form of a mountain lion emerging from the brush, her eyes trained on you. She pauses, still as marble, and you realize you are frozen where you stand. If you could think properly in this moment, you would distinctly feel a massive increase in your heart rate and a loud pulsing in your ears, along with a sharpening of your aural abilities. Inside your veins, blood would be rushing to your limbs and your heart, giving you the best physical chance to turn on your heels and run for your blessed life. These physiological responses are all gifts from our sympathetic nervous system. It is there to make sure you have the best possible chance at survival. It's function is to be on high alert, to rally the troops, to send in the battalions so that you can continue on. But here's the tricky bit: our sympathetic nervous system cannot tell the difference between actually being chased by a mountain lion and watching a film where we are so engrossed in the story that we *feel* as though we are being chased by a mountain lion. Taking this notion a step further, this aspect of our nervous system also cannot tell the difference between a physical threat to our lives and a deadline at work that has us so stressed out we've become a walking timebomb, frazzled and anxious and volatile. Sound familiar?

Then we have the parasympathetic nervous system, whose functions are rest and digest. This branch of the nervous system also exists to help us survive, but from the opposite end of the spectrum. It is there to assist us in transforming food into energy, recovering from a common cold or fighting off cancer cells. In order to heal ourselves, digest a meal, or sink into slumber, the parasympathetic nervous system must activate.

Now, here is where things get really interesting. What I'm about to say has become the epicenter of my wellness practice, and it's important, so listen up, y'all.

The sympathetic nervous system (fight or flight) and the parasympathetic nervous system (rest and digest) cannot be activated at the same time.

Translation: when we are in stress mode, we are literally not capable of reaching our optimal ability to heal.

Let us revisit the mountain lion tale (a tall tale, to be sure, but it clearly demonstrates my point). Allow me to add another detail to the story and submit that this walk was intended as a leisurely stroll to move your body after consuming a rather large and sumptuous lunch. I'll let you imagine what might have enjoyed at this festive occasion (Salad nicoise, perhaps? Café au lait? Crème brûlée for dessert? As you can see, my fantasy luncheon is situated in a quaint village tucked into the hills of southern France.) Regardless of what particular cuisine you might have enjoyed on this fateful day, you would have began the walk with your parasympathetic nervous system happily turned on, engaged in the business of relaxing your mind, soothing your heart, and assisting the various functions of your gastrointestinal tract for optimal energy attainment and nutrient absorption. However, the moment that growl pierced the afternoon silence, the sympathetic nervous system kicked into high gear, abruptly ending the blissful flow of tranquil regeneration and firing up like a Harley Davidson engine. The moment fear and stress becomes our dominant energy, we cease to rest and digest. That huge meal, for the moment, isn't going anywhere, because your body no longer cares about digesting when obviously the higher priority is saving your fragile, little life. Nutrients and minerals aren't of much use to a corpse.

This silly analogy, which I sincerely hope you never enact, is my way of expressing the dire importance of keeping our stress levels to a minimum, especially when attempting to focus our human superpowers on the simple yet mystical acts of digesting a meal or allowing our bodies to heal themselves. Each and every human holds an incredible capacity for healing, both in a simple resting state and in our ability to focus our minds toward positive thinking. We don't stand a chance, though, if we are not allowing the rest and digest mechanism to take hold. As long as we are in a state of stress, our ability to rest, digest, and heal ourselves lies dormant, completely useless.

DIET VS. LIFESTYLE

A fad can be defined as "a practice or interest followed for a time with exaggerated zeal."[13] We've all partaken in these short-lived crazes. Sometimes musical, sometimes fashionable, and most definitely edible, fads are just a given part of humans living amongst other humans. Someone comes up with a new idea or recycles an old one, gives it new life and new appeal, and a bunch of us invariably jump on the bandwagon; and for a time, this new thing, whatever it is, is *the* thing. And that is all good, because we are allowed to change our minds time and time again as we evolve. Sometimes, certain hues of these fads even stick. A child of the 80s and 90s, I myself will probably always be in love with a fluorescent pallet. No shame.

But if we want to, say, be healthy? Find our comfortable body shape? Feel at home in this physical vessel? Fads are not the best way to go. And I submit the following for your consideration: fad diets are futile if you are looking to create real, lasting change in your life. What can be said of dieting is that it inspires us to try new things and creates a playground to explore how certain foods or ways of eating affects us. Trial and error, after all, carries veritable clout. We can hear all the information there is on why this or that manner of eating is the *best* way, but nothing takes the place of first hand, anecdotal experience. If we are interested in embarking on this journey of creating a spiritual practice with our food, we must come back to the original definition of practice, which entails a long and drawn out commitment to repeated action. This commitment is not to a certain way of eating, but rather to the curiosity and attentiveness with which we approach our nourishment.

Let me clarify that I have no beef with any particular way of eating. There are shiny tokens of brilliance that can be found in paleo, macrobiotic, veganism and every other dietary theory that has been written about. While most of these methodologies have gone in and out of fashion in our culture at some point in time, in fact these ways of sustenance were created in culturally appropriate settings where there was a deep honoring of the geography and society which formed the method. Back in the Paleolithic era, the Caveman diet made a lot of sense because it was, in fact, born out of necessity. The important distinction here is the why. If we use a diet with the intention of manipulating our physical form into a particular shape, there is a good chance we are not understanding the true benefits of the diet, why it was created in the first place and most importantly, how to honor our bodies with it in a sustainable way. Following a vegan or gluten-free diet does not necessarily mean we are partaking in a fad.

Essentially, when our motivations for eating a certain way come from external sources, and not from a deep listening to our own body's needs and cravings, that is our signal we have fallen into a fad diet and may be neglecting our body's actual requirements for optimal health.

There is a certain respect, a true homage that takes place when we accept ourselves as we are in this moment. We are not static beings; rather, we are quite changeable. What feels right to you in this moment may not feel right tomorrow, let alone a month or year or decade from now. The simple fact is your body will change. Constantly. Be weary of dogmatic attitudes in the realm of food, for this leaves little to no room for the inevitable shifts we feel from our twenties to our fifties, or from spring to autumn, or even from morning to evening.

If you do find a certain way of eating that fits your body like a custom-made, couture leather glove, celebrate and embrace it! And then keep your mind open to the infinite possibility of changing circumstance.

There are two key ideas here to note. The first is to stay flexible and let your body expand, contract and morph as it most definitely will do, and eat accordingly to the signs you receive. Our bodies are incredibly wise and highly functioning, if we allow them to be so.

The second concept here that I wish to drive home and put securely to bed is that what works well for you may not work so well for your mother or best friend or neighbor. The Dalai Lama is one of my greatest personal heroes. He does not consume anything that came from an animal. While I deeply admire his commitment to this methodology and also understand his reasoning, my own body craves this kind of protein, and I choose not deprive it of what it asks for. Our guides and gurus exist to inspire us and push our boundaries, not to dictate how we live our lives. We are each unique individuals, and it is a plain fact that one diet will never, ever, ever work for everyone. Do not expect others to follow in your footsteps and receive the same results you do. We can only make suggestions, speak our truth, and keep our hearts open to infinite potential. That said, there are studies being done, research meticulously proven, and methodologies that may prove to assist you greatly in your path to wellness. The key is to stay curious. The moment we think we know is the moment of our greatest ignorance.

"FALL IN LOVE WITH THE TRUTH OF YOUR SHAPE"

Why do we care what we eat? Why do we want to "be healthy?"

Well, some of us don't. Most of us, however, do care. We care because we love our planet Earth. We care because we want to feel awake and alive and vital. We care because we want to be alive to support our children and our grandchildren. We care because we want to look good naked. Ahhh, yes. This is a big one. We care about what we eat because we want to look a certain way. And why do we want to look a certain way?

Most of us feel a deeply serious concern about our physical appearance. I believe that if this is our impetus to eat well, we will forever seek an idealized version of ourselves, and our food becomes a tool of manipulation rather than a celebration of delectable, sustaining life force.

One of my mottos is *forget about looking good naked, and focus on feeling good naked instead.* Here's what I mean: when we focus on the physical, we distort our vision. Let us revisit the earlier conversation about multi-tasking. When we put our attention on how we look in the mirror, how attuned are we to how it actually feels to be in our bodies?

The old adage *you are what you eat* is so true that anyone who disagrees is simply overlooking basic science. We take in nutrients, and those nutrients are the building blocks of our very cells, which together create a colony of cells which, when zoomed way out, take on the appearance of a human being. So yes, we are what we eat. But we are also HOW we eat, and WHY we eat.

There is a rarely discussed disease in this country leading to chronic unhappiness. I speak not of obesity or diabetes or inflammation; those are all obvious. I am talking about the disease of perfectionism. True, perfectionism is not a clinical term. But it undoubtedly causes dis-ease. In one of my most-treasured spiritual guidebooks, <u>The Four-Fold Way</u>, cultural anthropologist Angeles Arrien presents perfectionism as one of the four categories of universal addictions that humans are consumed by (the other three being the addiction to intensity, the addiction to needing to know, and the addiction to focusing on what is not working, rather than on what is working.)[14]

Here's an exercise: strip off all your garments and stand before a mirror. Take 5 minutes to really look. Look at all the angles, all the curves. Look at the hair. Look at the colors and tones and hues. Look at the height and length and width. Look at the ratios. Look at the textures. If you are an enlightened being, you will feel absolutely neutral or even delighted by every single detail you behold. It will be a private experience contained only within yourself, completely free of judgment or any absurd notion of external opinion. This is all imagined, by the way, because I am most certainly not an enlightened being. But this is my guide. Perhaps I'm making it up (in fact, I am absolutely making this up), but this is the ultimate goal in my heart— to see myself in my own naked truth, objectively.

Perhaps some of you are closer to enlightenment than you thought and this rings true for you? Bravo! Go get a chocolate-dipped ice cream cone and celebrate this enormous victory. More than likely, however, most of us do NOT in any way resonate with these sentiments. More than likely, as we scan the folds, plains and crevices of our bodily landscape, an overwhelming array of criticism floods our brain, painting our emotions pitch black with bitter vehemence.

Okay, if this describes you, please STOP. Please breathe. Take a moment to visualize the most adorable baby animal you've ever seen (Puppy? Kitten? Giraffe?) Derail the mind from the barrage of insults for just a moment. Please breathe some more. When you are ready, come back to yourself in the mirror, and pick one criticism. Just one. Be specific. Then ask yourself, why is this detail so disturbing to me? Where did I get the idea that something is wrong with this body?

Be honest. Where did the idea come from that you are not right, just as you are?

I one hundred percent guarantee that they did not come from you. They came from outside of you. Born out of a magazine cover, a cruel relative, a fictional novel, we believe we are not as we should be because we compare ourselves to one another, and because we believe the stories we hear. We believe so fervently that these mythologies become our truth.

Perhaps it is a lost cause, but allow me to attempt to soothe your pain with a question, inspired by a dear friend and yogic mentor Eddie Ellner, who constantly poses this question during his asana classes:

Can you begin to fall in love with the truth of your shape?

It IS within the realm of possibility to accept yourself as you are this very instant. That is truth. Whatever you see in that mirror is not only what you have to work with, it is also impermanent, changeable, and miraculous.

Even if you can only get yourself to the place of recognizing the story when it grips you, that is a wonderful beginning. Next time you shimmy into your swimwear and hear the nasty voices interrupt what might have otherwise been a fabulous day, please try to remember that you are being drawn into a narrative that does not belong to you. Put on a bikini, not a fairy tale. And smile, for goodness sake, because honestly, we take ourselves way too seriously.

PLEASURABLE PRACTICES

All great stories of transformation contain a hero. In my own journey towards health, the hero is none other than Ease. I acknowledge her (who is decidedly feminine in my narrative) because Ease was the energy with whom I chose to unite in all areas of my life. Her language is the law of attraction, of noticing the sign polls and saying yes when we are in a space of trust. When I joined forces with Ease, my life began to shift. When I allowed myself to say no to the things that did not align with my truth, ornate doorways began to appear and swing gracefully open, revealing secret gardens and mysterious temples within.

If this all sounds terribly mystical, let me break it down. Ease is a mistress of the water, which flows downstream at all times. Ease does not get into a rowboat and paddle against the current, sweating buckets and cursing when she doesn't make headway. The concept is simple: energy flows where attention goes. The law of attraction states that what we focus on, manifests. Whether we consciously want it to or not... Allow me to give you a very familiar yet disastrous example. Weight loss. The concept of "weight loss" is a classic situation where millions of people in

America focus their life energy, their hearts desire and lots of their hard-earned cash on losing weight. Here's the rub: the law of attraction does not hear the word "loss". It only attaches to the focus on weight. I literally cringe at the sound of "Weight Watchers." In terms of manifesting, that business could not be more poorly named. I realize the corporation referenced above is providing a huge support network to individuals nationwide who are sincerely struggling with their health and emotional well being. By no means do I intend to belittle the efforts of my fellow Americans working to slim down. Furthermore, I also recognize that Weight Watchers has intelligently altered its approach to more closely follow a path of least resistance. I will, however, state my genuine concern that counting calories or following a point system is not a lasting, sustainable solution to a healthier body. Such systems are built upon the diet paradigm, where you are encouraged to temporarily make rather drastic changes in your daily eating patterns until you have reached an idealized number on the scale that is your goal, the symbol of *healthy*. After you have arrived, then what? The moment these temporary eating patterns are softened or dropped altogether, the pounds return, the scale climbs, a feeling of failure and defeat setting in.

Compassionate I am to this cause, as despite being an incredibly athletic and active teenager, I carried extra weight on my body for over a decade. All the usual side effects— poor self-esteem, negative body image, fear of swimwear, constantly comparing myself to others— tinted my perception of the world. I saw myself as a healthy young woman who ate good food and exercised constantly, yet I struggled with excess weight that would not budge no matter how many miles I ran.

The real shift began to occur when I discovered hula hooping. I know, not the most poetic symbol of transformation. But it wasn't the act of hooping itself. It was, unbeknownst to me, that every time I picked up a hoop, turned on a song I loved and began to swing around in circles, I had pocket dialed Joy! I would completely lose track of time, and in an instant an hour had passed, all the while I had been swirling in delight, giggling at my errors, triumphing in my success as I mastered new tricks, and oh yes, I was drenched in sweat. Several years of this slow circular dance with Ease and the excess weight simply fell off of me. It wasn't a quick process with immediate results, but that is the epicenter of my point. I had not anticipated any results, besides pure, innocent enjoyment. As my shape began to morph, the beautiful face of Ease, in all her effortless, galavanting glory, came into focus. I grew increasingly curious about this concept, wondering where else I could apply this principle in my life.

When I ceased to put my attention on "working out" and "losing weight" and put my attention instead on enjoying myself and feeling good in my body, clouds parted.

I saw the light, and it shone brilliantly down upon this newly discovered truth: feeling good is not work. It cannot be made into labor, for the moment we force ourselves onto an idea, we are back in that rowboat, paddling upstream and going nowhere.

I have since applied the principle of Ease to my friendships, my intimate relationship, my diet and even my vocation. I found myself walking a path of holistic healthcare by saying yes, one invitation at a time. I first glimpsed nutrition as a missing puzzle piece, thinking it would be a nice accompaniment to my work as a yoga teacher, plant medicine practitioner and aromatherapist. I had no clue that in fact I would come to see nutrition as the table upon which the entire puzzle is built. And I now approach my diet just as I do my exercise— I listen to my body and do my best everyday to do as it asks of me. And I enjoy myself! I move in ways that bring me pleasure. I eat foods that are deliciously nourishing to my body, spirit and soul, making choices based on how I feel. I laugh as much as possible, and spend my time around people who bring me joy, peace and insight. I surround myself with objects I adore and live in an environment that fills my heart with serenity and inspiration.

My life is not perfect, nor do I believe in such a thing. Perfection is a myth and I strive to be present with what is, relishing in the ability to create my reality with the simple decisions I make. We are all capable of this very real magic. Ease is not a spell, she is a dear friend. I choose to walk with her as often as possible.

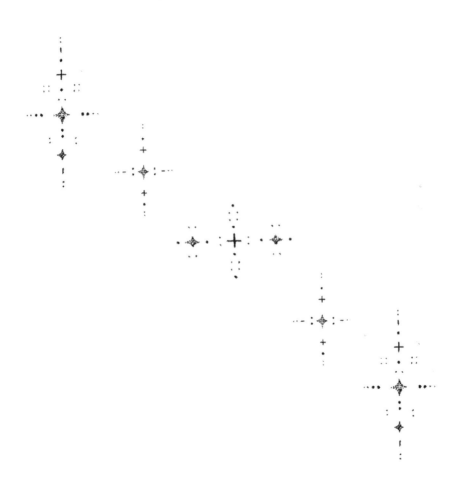

CHAPTER 5
EARTHLY DELIGHTS

A SUSTAINABLE KITCHEN

We cannot discuss the act of eating without getting into a conversation about our marvelous planet. Long enough have we put a vast canyon between ourselves and the origin of the foods on which we survive. The chronic dissociation from the contents of our plate symbolizes something much deeper than ignorance, for we have literally left the fields of our crops to the fate of our consumer culture. But the outcome is not predestined, as we are the ultimate decision makers. Our preference for convenience and our priority of the bottom line has led to a lack of transparency and integrity. This is a topic that has somehow become oddly controversial, despite its blatant necessity.

In this dialogue, let us focus not on the grandiose vision of saving the planet (which quickly spirals into a deeply depressing black hole of doom), but on the heroically subtle ways we can make a real difference, one action at a time.

Following is a list of simple ideas to create a sustainable kitchen from which you can prepare sacred nourishment, aligning your vitality with that of the earth which we embrace and call home.

1. Reduce your plastic

Many of us purchase items in plastic regularly, assuring ourselves that these items are recyclable. Allow me to clarify this issue of recycling plastic. Some types of plastic are easy to recycle while others are not, and there are more buyers for some plastics than for others, which means recycling facilities have incentivized motives for processing various types of plastics.[15]

Check your city's website to see which types of materials they accept for recycling. Placing non or soiled recyclables in with the legit stuff can actually contaminate an entire batch of items, resulting in no buyers for that repurposed plastic, which then ends up in a landfill. Or the ocean. If you want some truly unappetizing motivation for buying less plastic, search Google for "Pacific Ocean Garbage Patch."[16] Ironically, most food items and packaging are stamped with a recycling symbol, even if they are not accepted for recycling! Talk about false advertising.

In addition to the recycling conundrum, plastics are also potentially harmful, as they can leach harsh hormone-influencing chemicals into their contents. In particular, be on high alert for the chemicals bisphenol A (BPAs) and phthalates, which have been linked to such health problems as deformed genitals, premature puberty, decreased sperm quality, cancers of the reproductive organs, fertility and birth complications, diabetes, allergies and neurological disorders.[17] The European Union, along with many other countries, actually banned phthalates in 2005; yet we here in the good ol' USA still employ them freely and frequently in many of our plastics that contain our edibles.

Action-Oriented Strategies to reduce your plastic:

- If there is no recycling symbol on the plastic, odds are it is not recyclable (a few examples: trash bags, ziplocks, bubble wrap, the plastic bags inside cereal boxes, plastic wrap, potato/tortilla chip bags, candy wrappers, bagged lettuce mixes). See if you can find an alternative in a recyclable container, or use the bulk bins.

- Even if your local guidelines don't specify that you need to clean out that almond butter jar before you toss it in the bin, please do it anyway. Plastic bottles, bags or containers that are soiled will contaminate the recycling stream. If they are not able to be cleaned (this sadly applies to moldy or oil-soaked pizza boxes as well), please throw them in the trash.

- Check with your local recycling facility so you can be clear on which items you can and cannot put in the blue bin. Though many items are difficult or not financially feasible to recycle into other products, technology is advancing and hopefully we will continue to see more options available to us.

- Do not put hot foods or liquids into plastic containers unless they are BPA and phthalate-free.

- Buy yourself a glass or metal water bottle. Befriend it! Take good care of it and perhaps acquire several sizes so you can always have one on you regardless of the size of your satchel or purse. (for more on the divine importance of water consumption, read the Habit of Hydration chapter.)

- Keep reusable grocery bags in your car (I recommend canvas ones, as they last longer and can be laundered to remove the inevitable remnants from your excursion to the farmer's market.

- Brainstorm ways to use less plastic!

2. Get Into Glass

Say hello to your kitchen's new best friend. Glass is made from completely natural, raw, sustainable materials. For those of us concerned about what chemicals might be leaching into our food and drinks through lab-made plastics, glass is the highly preferred choice. Glass is the only widely-used packaging material considered "GRAS" (generally recognized as safe) by the U.S. Food and Drug Administration. It's also 100% recyclable and can be reused endlessly with no loss in quality or purity.[18]

Ah, infinitely recyclable. Now that's a concept I can get behind.

Action-Oriented Strategies to use glass:

- Get yourself a glass (or metal, depending on your preference) water bottle. Begin to think twice before buying plastic water bottles. Move the priority of having water accessible to you at all times to the top of your necessary health to-do list.

- Get yourself a set of glass food storage containers for your kitchen. They are awesome, look nice, don't scratch, don't warp, are safe to use with hot items and can even be thrown in the oven to warm up leftovers. And they will last a LOT longer than their plastic counterparts.

- Have a collection of glass jars in an assortment of sizes. The classic Mason jar is a kitchen necessity and has endless uses, including canning and preserving, leftover food storage, use as a glass, making sprouts... You get the idea. The hipsters and the hippies embraced the glass jar and made it cool again. You can too.

- Most of us have access to at least one local health food store where we can fill liquid items from bulk bins (honey, olive oil, hand or dish soap). Build a little collection of various sized glass bottles and jars that you love aesthetically, then take them with you to the grocery store and fill your own bottles instead of buying new ones. Don't forget to tare the weight on your way in, or bring an extra for reference at checkout.

- Keep an eye out for glass containers of all shapes and sizes at antique and thrift stores, and estate or yard sales. This brings the recycling concept one level deeper as you are now the recycler. Plus, these repurposed items are imbued with their previous life's magic; they look funky or classy or vintage, and are way more interesting than buying new; can be used for storage on counters in your kitchen, bathroom or bedroom, as well as for serving or cooking food. You might find you have a certain style you want to utilize in your home (opaque white milk glass or green colored glass, for example) for which you can always be on the hunt.

3. Create a user-friendly system for recyclables, trash and compost

Keep it simple. Find containers that you like, that fit your space and that make the process of properly disposing of items easy. We are much more likely to actually take advantage of these various ways to dispose of our used items if we make it realistic for ourselves.

<u>**Action-Oriented Strategies for proper disposal:**</u>

- Use containers that can be easily cleaned, as all three categories of these vessels tend to get sludgy, smelly and generally quite nasty over time. Opt for glass, ceramic or metal over plastic (duh!)

- If you're new to compost, you can buy a simple compost bin to sit in your yard. There are all sorts of various models available today, from countertop composters to rotating back yard contraptions to building a wooden box, keeping a bucket of dried material to toss on top nearby and throwing a piece of plywood over it as a lid. And if you really cannot be bothered to compost (really?), then find out if your city offers a green bin option for your green waste. These bins are generally used for yard waste such as mowed grass and plant clippings, but can also be used for food remnants.

- Taking that last suggestion one more step, keep your fridge clean so you don't lose your leftovers in the cold abyss and can actually consume them before they rot. Or, if you know for a fact that you don't like to eat leftover food (really?), learn how to make the quantities that you and your household will eat in one sitting. Become a master of necessary portions.

4. Quality over quantity

This is a very general suggestion that easily applies to any and all areas of our vast human life. By choosing quality over quantity in terms of our needs for food preparation, storage and consumption, we leave a notably smaller carbon footprint upon the earth.

<u>Action-Oriented Strategies to choose quality over quantity:</u>

- A great example of this idea is dish soap. I have found that many "natural" dish soaps seem to be much less concentrated and sudsy compared to the traditional neon blue brands. But if you are not willing to use the toxic stuff (bravo), and therefore going through a bottle of soap much quicker, that means you're also purchasing (and therefore tossing) more containers. Experiment and find the brands that you like best, that work for you and have the longest life. In case you're wondering about dish soap recommendations, I am a huge fan of Sals Suds by Dr. Bronners. Order it in bulk and refill a fancy glass bottle with a spout or pump lid that lives beside your kitchen sink.

- Apply this same principle to dishes, drinking glasses and silverware. You may need to spend a bit more to get a higher quality, longer lasting product. That also means you won't need to replace them nearly as often. Plus, if you choose pieces and collections that you absolutely love, you aren't as likely to keep buying even though you already have enough to supply your household and regular flow of guests (unless you are like my mother, who requires multiple sets of dishes and table settings to satiate her artistry and accommodate her frequent dinner parties).

- Same thing goes for dish towels, sponges, and rags. This would be an opportune moment to invite you to reduce your use of paper towels. Linens are lovely, and can be washed and reused until they are worn through, which usually takes a number of years. Choosing darker colors can be a good way to go, as whites, pastels and lighter tones get stained and tainted much quicker. If these colors are a necessary part of your aesthetic, then so be it (I love white myself), just be aware of how often you are replacing these items and perhaps use them a bit more sparingly or occasionally.

5. Use earth-friendly cleaning products, or make your own

Our economy is based on consumption, so I do not blame you if you have never even considered the notion that you could, in fact, make your own all-purpose cleaner. But hey, here is a radical concept: you can! Most cleaning supplies we use these days, and in fact most products we use in our homes in general (that includes our self-care and beauty products) can be made using simple, whole foods and totally safe, natural, non-toxic ingredients. And in your reusable glass jars and bottles, no less! Now we are really getting somewhere!!!

<u>**Action-Oriented Strategies to replace toxic products:**</u>

- You can save money and plastic, avoid toxins and feel like a superhero by making your own household cleaners. Nearly any cleanser you can imagine can be made with a few simple ingredients (dish tabs, floor cleaner, window spray, all-purpose cleaners, laundry detergent and boosters, stain removers, carpet cleaners... you get the idea).

- Here's a list of staple ingredients to collect for formulating your own alchemical cleansing products:
  - Baking soda
  - White and apple cider vinegar
  - Lemon juice
  - Castile soap
  - Borax
  - Essential Oils

- You can pretty much clean your entire house with baking soda, vinegar and lemon juice. To find easy recipes you can put into use immediately, hop on Google or even better, Pinterest.com. There you will find a treasure trove of cleansing wisdom to keep your space spotless for the rest of your days.

6. Get yourself some high quality Essential Oils

Acquiring a collection of top shelf essential oils is an incredible investment for your home and the health of your entire family. Do you know what "natural flavoring" and "perfume" means? Me neither! Because these nonspecific umbrella terms used by the food, supplement and beauty industry don't actually tell us anything about what is in those products. The insane truth is that the term *natural flavoring* is completely nondescript, but this single mystery ingredient can be found in almost all of our foods! Added flavoring, both natural and artificial, can contain anywhere from 50 to 100 ingredients. And "natural flavoring" is the fourth most common ingredient listed on labels! Furthermore, "natural" and "artificial" flavoring may not be all that different, and can potentially be harmful to our health.[19]

Being savvy about our ingredients all the sudden seems like a nearly impossible task.

Essential oils (henceforward referred to as "EOs") are fantastic because, if you buy a high quality brand, they contain just one ingredient:

pure essential oil that has been steam distilled from plants. And we are able to reap all the benefits of that plant's medicinal properties when we use its essential oils. Quality definitely matters here, and I recommend certain brands over others, dōTERRA® being my personal brand of choice. Living Libations® and Florecopia® are also exquisite. Do your research. Even if you think, well I'm just using it to clean my toilet, what does it matter if it is chemical or natural based? For one thing, that water is going down the drain to join with the water table. For another thing, you're inhaling it as you shine up that porcelain temple, and lastly, you will be sitting your bare bottom on top of it in due time, so what ingredients would you prefer to be absorbing through the skin of that particularly intimate area?

Action-Oriented Strategies for using EOs:

- Beauty and self-care products are an ideal place to focus on drastically reducing your toxic load. Happily, you'll also reduce the money you spend and amount of containers you use for the many products you bring into your home. Again, try a search on

Pinterest for some DIY recipes. I also love the <u>Aromatherapy Handbook for Beauty, Hair, and Skin Care</u> by Erich Keller.

- Here are just a few self-love products to try making yourself with EOs:

  o Soaps

  o Bath bombs

  o Facial moisturizers, cleansers and toners

  o Body butter

  o Deodorant

  o Toothpaste

- Get yourself a diffuser! Diffusers use water to create a superfine mist, propelling the essential oil molecules into the atmosphere, effectively purifying the air, keeping airborne bacteria at bay, and eliminating foul odors, as well as enhancing your mood and nervous system with aromatherapy. They are marvelous! I keep one next to my bed, one on my desk, and bring one to use with clients during sessions or into the studio when I'm teaching a yoga class. Use different oils for different purposes (lavender to calm and wild orange to uplift, for instance).

- To learn more on which oils to use for what purpose, I like the book <u>Modern Essentials.</u>

- If you want to learn more about essential oils, what to look for in a brand or where to buy the high quality ones, check out my website or contact me for a consultation.

7. Watch your water usage

I have a specific memory of being at a girlfriend's house doing dishes after a dinner party, and her schooling me on the amount of water I was using. While I could have gotten defensive and let my ego rage about being told I was doing something wrong, instead her words stuck with me and struck a deep chord that I carry with me to this day.

Water is our true medicine. It is the real deal, our life force, and we would not last long without it. It is probably our most valuable natural resource. That being said, there are an awfully large number of areas on the planet in severe drought and extreme water shortage. The invitation here is quite simple: please bring more awareness to how you use water. If possible, make it a practice to give this element your deepest respect. When you can, cut down on the amount you use, the pressure from the faucet, and the amount that is going down the drain untouched.

<u>Action-Oriented Strategies to build awareness around your water usage:</u>

- Place a small hand-written sign or image next to your sink to remind you to keep the pressure on low while doing dishes.

- Use a biodegradable dish soap (I love Dr. Bronner's Sals Suds) so you aren't contributing to toxicity entering your local water table.

- Use a wash and rinse bin while doing dishes, and recycle the water by feeding it to some trees or plants outside.

- Most toilets these days are water-saving designs. You can also place a full bottle of water in the tank to displace some of the water that refills with each flush.

- Turn off the faucet while you are brushing your teeth. (Bonus tip: according to Nadine Artemis of Living Libations, you actually get more benefit if you do not wet your toothbrush before putting it to work on your teeth and gums. Just sayin'.)

- Wash your face with a washcloth and a bowl of warm water instead of letting the warm water flow down the drain. Again, you can toss this water into a nearby garden and water some thirsty plants.

- Install soaker hoses on timers to feed your gardens. Same thing with sprinklers. Make sure you are putting water where you want it to go.

- And for the love of all things holy, if you live in a dry area, please do not have a lawn of grass. I lived in Los Angeles for several years and there is nothing more ironic than a green lawn in L.A. Except perhaps a green lawn in Las Vegas.

- Hire a native plant landscaper to come to your home and do a consultation with you. They can offer some sustainably wise ideas on cutting down on your water consumption by choosing plants that require an amount of water in alignment with your geographic location.

8. Save the trees! Pair down on paper.

I cannot tell you how crazy it makes me to go into a public restroom and watch people pull 2, 3 or 4 paper towels from the dispenser, only to give their hands a swift pat dry and toss the mostly huge dry bundle into the trash.

<u>**Action-Oriented Strategies to reduce paper usage:**</u>

- Watch the TED talk by Joe Smith on How to Use A Paper Towel.[20] Then send it to everyone you know. It is not that we are stupid. We are just ignorant. Let's help one another out.

- As mentioned above, if you decide to keep paper towels in your kitchen, use them for a very limited number of purposes. A roll of paper towels can last us a very long time. Have an extensive collection of rags and use them to clean your kitchen, wipe up spills, dry off your cast iron pans and other such applications.

- Keep an array of cloth napkins. My parents have a fun assortment of napkin rings, which keep the napkins tidy in between meals, but also serve the purpose of designating whose napkin is whose, so that you can re-use them for multiple meals until you determine they actually need to be washed.

9. Find your local farmers

Odds are high that most of us have at least one farmers market near our neighborhood. I love supporting my local farmers for many reasons. Meeting the folks who actually grow and harvest our food brings us closer to the earth and the labor-intensive process of feeding ourselves. By paying the farmers directly, we eliminate the middleman, giving more of our money to the people caretaking the land, and therefore we do not give that money to larger corporations where we would likely otherwise buy our groceries. Attending a market is a community-building activity, where upon repetition, we recognize our neighbors, become friendly with our favorite vendors and have an opportunity to ask questions about how and where our food comes from.

Action-Oriented Strategies to support local farms:

- Locate all the farmer's markets in your area, then make a weekly ritual of them! Often, towns or cities have websites where all the various markets are listed with days, times and locations, so you can be fully aware of all your options.

- Make a date of it! Put on a festive shirt and a nice hat, round up several of your canvas grocery bags and a friend or two, and take your time. Meander. Amble. Enjoy the vibe of like-minded folks gathering together to honor the act of nourishing ourselves. If you're an artist, bring along a camera or buy some ingredients for a still life. Endless inspiration lives in the aisles of our farmer's markets. Be open to cultivating newfound appreciation for your food.

- Challenge yourself to buying a new food you've never cooked before. Don't know what to do with it? Look up a recipe.

- Check out local Community Supported Agriculture options. CSAs are a fantastic way to support your local farming industry, eat with the seasons and become intimately familiar with your local fare. As we build relationships with our farmers, we also deepen our comprehension of sustainable accessibility to foods in our region.

- Look outside the box! You may be able to find a seafood CSA if you live near the ocean, a local mushroom farm or gatherer, cheese and dairy products, as well as buying meat from your neighborhood farm. Often there are options to go in on an entire animal with several other folks, which will stock your freezer in an affordable way and give you a profound peace of mind that your meat is coming from a reputable, trustworthy source.

10. Enough is enough

Quite simply, let us begin to buy what we need. While grocery shopping, take into consideration how many people you feed on a daily basis, and the storage capacity of your refrigerator, freezer and pantry. In Europe, it is quite common to shop several times throughout the week, if not daily. I am not suggesting this is the right way, but it is certainly on the opposite end of the spectrum from a trip to Costco, and worth considering. We all have individual needs, and honoring those needs is important. It is also important to experiment with various methodologies. We humans have a tendency to get stuck in our particular ways of functioning, simply because they are familiar and bring us comfort. There are numerous profound and often repeated quotes on stepping outside of our comfort zone, but I think I'll go with this: "a ship in a harbor is safe, but that is not what a ship is built for."[21]

THE PROXIMITY FACTOR

Have you ever stopped to consider how many miles your morning banana travelled to grace your breakfast table? We are blessed today with the opportunity to eat nearly any food, any time we desire it. This is possible through the massive transport industry that has risen up around edibles, carting tropical fruits to cold weather climates with such regularity and frequency that it is easy to forget the source of such tasty goodness. I enjoy the plump, glistening, fleshy sweetness of a mango as much as anyone, so in this chapter I merely suggest we take pause and appreciate where our food hails from; giving thanks to the lands far and wide producing our daily 'necessities' that we so often take for granted, and perhaps contemplating life without those so-called staples.

Increasing our mindfulness of our food's origin includes three factors: knowing where our food was grown, the type of labor required to grow and harvest it, and the amount of resources required to transport it around the globe. Some of us may be swift to criticize the oil industry and all its questionably unethical practices, yet complain about the price of our pineapple. Whether we like it or not, we must accept that we are partaking in this very big business when we indulge in foreign fare or even a domestically produced item grown across our own sprawling country.

Furthermore, there is a theme of estrangement that unifies many of the subjects in this book. The separation from what is on our plate, when magnified, reveals itself as a dissociation from the land we inhabit. If we deny our connectedness to this earth, we are free to continue making choices and shunning the responsibility that accompanies them. Procuring a perfectly manicured, well-dressed, cellophane and Styrofoam encapsulated raw chicken hardly resembles the bird itself, and many of us would likely rethink our purchase were it to appear less pretty, sterile and safely non-violent in its packaging. This statement merely brings us to an invitation to look closer at the choices we make in the aisles of our grocery store. What did this creature or morsel look like as a living, thriving element of nature? How might it have been processed? Can you imagine the steps taken to transform it from its raw state to the box, bag or package you hold in your hand? The further away we get from simple, easily imagined steps, the closer we come to a heavily manufactured processing of our foods. Most likely, this process will not only entail adding preservatives and other unnecessary ingredients, but we lose a large amount of the original nutrients in both the processing and the time passing between harvest and consumption.

Eating locally is a key element in this spiritual food practice equation. Calling upon the resources already close at hand offers us a chance to connect more authentically to our own homeland, wherever that may be. It also presents an interesting opportunity to confront our cravings and ask the question, do I live in the appropriate environment to support the type of food my body loves?

For example, if you know for a fact that your body thrives on the lush, sweet, juicy fruits of the tropics, and you live on the east coast of the United States, perhaps now would be an felicitous time to seriously consider renting a place in Mexico or Hawaii and spending part of your year there. This may sound like an outlandish suggestion, but why not? You could reframe this possibility as honoring your body's needs and desires! Why force ourselves to exist in an environment that doesn't feel like home? Home is a place that meets you exactly where you need to be met, bringing you precisely the seasonal shifts, weather patterns, community structure and edible offerings that are a match for your body, soul and spirit. More often than not, I see folks who are not satisfied with their regional residence in the world, yet accept it obligingly and with an air of resignation. Fortunate we are here in the United States to have freedom to move about as we are so inclined, so I invite you to really contemplate if your home meets your deepest needs for everything a home can be. Let us not underestimate the wisdom of our bodies. We all carry around a lifetime of experiences within us, and, if your mind is open to some Buddhist thought, many lifetimes of experience. These experiences shape us far more than we realize, and too often we force ourselves into a predetermined life, rather than take the helm of our own magnificent ship.

So how to implement all of this? Start small. Prepare one meal a week with ingredients solely found at your local farmer's market, just to give yourself a nice plunge into the cool waters of reality. You may be delighted at the abundant proliferation of options! Or, you may feel dismayed at your lack of usual go-to favorites. This is an opportunity to get creative, look up a recipe for kohlrabi or kabocha squash or pork belly, and get real with yourself. At the very least, try on awareness. You may be surprised how far you can travel one tiny step at a time.

HOW TO HARVEST

Several years past, I attended a primitive-skills gathering. If you have never heard of such a thing, it is well worth investigating; sort of like a summer camp where all the activities are fundamental survival crafts and techniques. Basket weaving, hide tanning, archery and tracking are a few examples of what you might experience at such an event. I heard a Chumash elder speak on the importance of harvesting plants with respect, and his words lodged themselves in my subconscious. His message was that all living things deserve our utmost respect and honor, including the plants all around us.

Instead of picking, pulling or cutting down plants with thoughtless abandon, we can stop for a moment and commune with the spirit of that plant, express gratitude and ask for permission.

I love this concept.

Reach out with your eyes and take in the colors, curves and angles of the leaves, the sturdiness of the stalk, the arm-like formations of the branch. Reach out with your hands and touch the soft fuzz, the crisp smoothness, the supple blossom. Inhale the earthy aroma, be it sweet, pungent, or spicy. Allow your spirit to commune and exchange greetings with the spirit of this plant before you. Strike up a rousing, silent conversation. The intelligence of plants is nearly beyond our comprehension, and yet we pluck their physical forms at will without attempting to grasp the miraculous meaning of their many gifts.

"If you love a flower, don't pick it up. Because if you pick it up,
it dies and it ceases to be what you love. So if you love a
flower, let it be. Love is not about possession. Love is about
appreciation."

— Master Zen teacher Thich Nat Hahn

While most of us will likely continue to bring cut flowers into our homes, let this suggestion reside somewhere in your heart. Seek its wisdom, and let yourself determine where balance can be found.

FACE YOUR FOOD

Likewise, to harvest an animal is also to take the life of a living being. I myself am an omnivore, and though I do not claim that any one way is the correct path, I do believe we can treat the lives we sacrifice to nourish our own with due respect, honor, and compassion.

I once harvested a turkey for Thanksgiving. I chose to do this because I felt it important to offer my gratitude directly, to take this experience literally into my own hands and let it steep into my memory, and to see how this would affect my inclination towards carnivorousness.

My sweetheart and I found a farm nearby offering an annual "Face Your Food" workshop. Wandering around the land, I beheld the mighty birds that were to be my feast the following Thursday, and somehow I had never fully appreciated their beauty. The iridescent blue-green shimmer around their eyes and face, the brilliant red of their comb, the majesty of their deep shining feathers, and my oh my, they are large beasts. It was entirely up to me to select my turkey and hold his great body in my trembling arms as I prepared myself for the task ahead. For several quiet minutes, our hearts beat together. Then, carefully following expertly practiced instruction, I hung him upside down. We held his wings down and eased his large body through a 5-gallon bucket with a hole cut in the bottom, out which his oddly wrinkled head emerged, eyes wide and steadily blinking. I did my best to hold my hand steady as I pulled the thick, red scaly skin away from his body and sliced my knife through the large vein in his throat. I held him and stroked his feathers as blood first cascaded, then dripped, into a second waiting orange bucket. As the life left him, his eyes looked directly into mine, as if he knew why I had come here, and it was his last mission to see this through with me. I do not deny that I longed to sever the disquiet surging through my body. Waves of sorrow and compassion and remorse and gratitude took me again and again as I sat with him, pummeling me against death's gritty shores. It wasn't as swift as I would have liked. Several minutes passed in slow agony, and I continued to breath; inhale, exhale, repeat, again and again.

Finally, his wings stilled, his heart stopped, and his spirit lifted, vanished, leaving a remnant vacant expression and a warm, very large, utterly beautiful, dead bird.

I relive this experience as I write about it, and though I still eat meat to this day, I also feel the sting of reality. When we buy a chicken breast encased neatly in clear plastic and Styrofoam, we are so far removed from what that animal looked like alive, let alone how it lived and how it was harvested. If there is one area in our food where we can be more mindful, I will always recommend to start with the meat and dairy we buy. Not only do we consume toxins and hormones when we buy factory-farmed meat, but we ingest the trauma of that animal's life. We are what we eat, and what we eat becomes us. Please, choose wisely, and with full transparency. Waking up means that we might not like what we see, but it also means we deepen our capability to choose differently. Enough of us making a different choice is all we need to swing the pendulum of supply and demand.

And if you are called to take on the experience of harvesting an animal, I say yes. For those of us who are meat-eaters, there is really nothing to lose; we only stand to strengthen our integrity, our responsibility and our respect for ourselves and other beings.

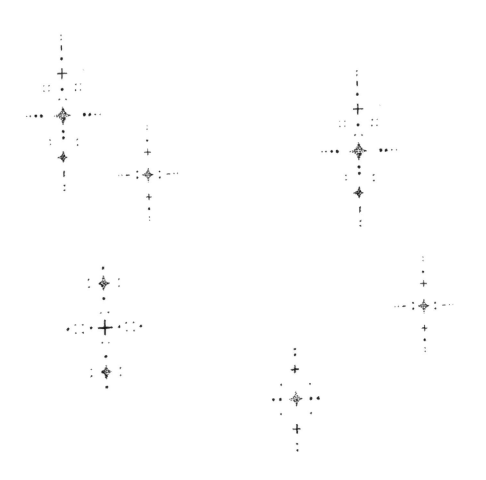

CHAPTER 6
THE WHOLE TRUTH

In July of 2016, my beloved and I embarked upon something so fraught, so perilous, so intimidating, most humans would simply scoff at the mere idea. It's called an elimination diet. And no, it is not all about poop (though of course, that is a major theme.)

Here is the premise, as presented by author of <u>The Elimination Diet</u>, Tom Malterre: what we eat everyday, on a regular basis, is our primary source of nutrition, and thus it is also our primary source of irritation.[22] Remove all the foods which most commonly and frequently irritate the human body in our world today for several weeks, allowing the gut to calm down and come back into balance; then reintroduce each category of food one at a time to see what happens. The process is broken up into three phases (detox phase, elimination phase, and reintroduction phase) and takes a minimum of two months to complete if followed exactly. Over the span of the experimental journey, it is recommended to keep a strict food diary, recording everything that enters your mouth (edibles, that is) and any reactions, effects or symptoms.

Why did I walk forth willingly into such an undertaking? Well there are several reasons, but the simplest one is curiosity. I have so many friends who are gluten-intolerant, lactose-intolerant, vegan and so on, and I wanted to know the truth of myself, for myself. A food allergy is different from a food sensitivity. Experiencing no obvious signs of food allergies (hives, for example, or swelling in my throat to the point of not being able to inhale), the only noticeable symptom I consistently suffer from is headaches, so that was my main inquiry: was something I ate regularly creating brain pain? One way to find out.

Here are the foods we eliminated from our diet: beef, pork, dairy, nuts, peanuts, eggs, shellfish, sesame seeds, caffeine, alcohol, chocolate, yeast, wheat, gluten, soy, sugar and corn. Reading deeper into this list, what this process really entails is the removal of all processed foods, as the number of hidden ingredients and preservatives are countless, additionally accounting for the contamination factor from shared equipment and amount of pesticides, additives and artificial ingredients commonly found in most packaged foods. A clean, fresh diet of whole foods; that is what I committed myself to for what ended up being three months.

I have never eaten so well in my entire life. I have never cooked so often in my entire life. And I have never spent so much money on groceries. One day I was visiting a friend who asked me how the "deprivation diet" was going. I laughed heartily and assured him that I was anything but deprived! Instead of attempting to walk you through that season of solidarity, I will offer an excerpt from my journal, to give you a taste of how I felt soon after its conclusion:

These past two weeks have been an emotional foray into what it must be like to be a person diagnosed with bipolar disorder. Some mornings, I've found myself sitting in a deeply meditative state, spiraling upwards into a vast span of sparkling creative flow, and my heart is cracking open and spilling copious amounts of joyful gratitude for this majestic life of humble grandeur I am so privileged to live. Several hours later, slumped over my laptop, I plummet into a cavern of despair, dragged down by the ankles and held there; literally depressed by the weight of some unseen force that has lodged in my belly and spread its evil tentacles into each limb, toe and follicle of my being. Lurking in cold, dank waters, a darkness expands like a cloud of black ink. The source of this seemingly eternal abyss is not a giant squid; rather, it is that delicious cup of coffee I had for breakfast. The ink is not ink, but molecules of caffeine, seeping into my consciousness, rudely shaking me asleep under a blanket of dark fog.

Caffeine was not the only substance I discovered to be troublesome. Corn, almonds, cashews, peanuts, gluten and yeast topped the list of digestive perpetrators. I could go on to give a full progress report, grading each food for its particular offensiveness, but the greater lesson from this experience lies in the responsibility of knowing for a fact that my body reacts poorly to a certain substance, and then actually making choices to support those findings.

When I completed the three-month long elimination diet, I had a one or two-week period in a state of quasi-denial, pretending that I was still just "experimenting" with the foods that had already given me grief. Because they were familiar. Because they were my old fallback comfort foods. Because they are commonplace, and tasty, and easy. Making choices that best support my body is not always easy. This I consider to be the unofficial fourth phase of the Elimination Diet: the backlash phase. This is when, despite everything I've just spent copious amounts of hours, effort and dollars to learn about myself, I throw it all out the window and act the fool; unknowing, blissfully ignorant, peacefully strolling, with bulletproof coffee and almond croissant in hand, right off a cliff. I keep thinking of the Spiderman story, when Peter Parker's uncle Ben gets shot by a robber and, just before dying, mutters his last lovingly patronizing words to his nephew, "with great power comes great responsibility." Knowledge is power, and thus this embodied knowledge feels like an entirely new food group I am literally struggling to digest.

But what an adventure! Amidst my constipation and grouchiness, the light peeks out from behind the trees and I remind myself that it's really not so bad. We are so attached to our relationship with the foods we eat that we often forget we eat to live, not the other way around. The greatest gift I could receive from this experience is the courage to select my sustenance with an intention of kindness in my heart. This is the body I have had since birth, and it shall carry me into the last moment of this lifetime. Why not give it the best chance to thrive? Why not treat it as I would treat a precious item of clothing, which it is. A glorified meat-suit, wired and connected to nerves, emotions and a brain. And, and, my friends, it is transitory. This body and all its innerworkings are temporary. I am a spiritual being having a human experience, and thus, I can loosen my grip a bit. I can choose to make these decisions with my well-being in mind. I can allow myself to unclench the fisted almond butter sandwich. There are so many other fabulously splendidly enticingly scrumptious options. It is a new day. I choose to feel well, to eat well, to be well. It may be a big pill to swallow, but that's what knives and cutting boards are for.

THE WHOLE TRUTH

One of the simplest ways to improve your overall health is to shift your daily nutritional intake towards eating more whole foods. I'm sure you've heard that one before! The nearly mythological "whole food" sometimes feels shrouded in mystery and deceit. Indeed, the number of labels proudly proclaiming their packaged product as such is rather numerous, and yet in truth, many of these edibles are a far cry.

Let's get into it.

A whole food is just what it sounds like— a food that is intact and along the further end of the unprocessed spectrum. Dried beans, though they have been dehydrated, belong in this category, as they remain as they were when harvested from their source. Whole grains, a term as abused as tobacco, literally mean a grain that is still whole (complex, I know!) So why does a box of Lucky Charms proclaim to contain "whole grains"? Truths can be stretched and stretched like melty mozzarella, and many brands do whatever it takes to market themselves as healthful products. A pulverized grain is technically not a whole food, and then if you add food coloring, artificial flavors, preservatives, sugars, and a host of other chemically-based ingredients, you have wandered off the map.

Michael Pollan calls this genre "edible food-like substances"[4] and I love him for it. Let his loquacious description be a reminder to remain in the sphere of the real. An easy way to gauge how whole a food truly is: simply read the ingredients. Look for foods that contain less than five ingredients. A single item ingredient list is the epitome of a whole food. You could buy granola that is made from simple, whole foods, or you could buy granola loaded with shrouded additives. Best option? Buy a beauteous array of whole foods — seeds, nuts, oats, dried fruit— and make your own damn granola! Easy, quick, cheap and the best perk of all is that you know and love every little thing in it.

Though it is likely evident by this time, I must state the obvious here: not everything sold in a Whole Foods Market is a whole food. In fact, these and other natural grocery stores carry just as many processed "edible food-like items" as your average large chain. These days, when I'm in the checkout line at Whole Foods, I often find myself gazing around in wonder, peering into the baskets and carts of my fellow shoppers. Do not be fooled by marketing, for it is their job to entice you with flashy, attractive language, and they are very good at it! Tortilla chips, no matter how organic, are not a whole food. Does that mean you should not eat them? Absolutely not. Just be aware, and be honest with yourself. If you seek better health through nutrition, seek simple, whole, real, fresh foods. This is also an invitation to get into the kitchen more frequently, so I will make this subsequent claim very plain: If you seek better health through nutrition, cooking is non-negotiable. There are only so many whole foods that can be eaten without preparation. This desire in you to lose weight, have more energy, sleep deeper, and feel more joy, is asking you for accountable action. There is no shortcut to health. Which brings us back to the very essence of this book.

We must eat, every day, multiple times per day. If we desire to feel our very best so that we can show up in the world and be of service, giving our original and much-needed gifts, we must eventually arrive in the kitchen; sleeves rolled, knives sharpened, hands washed, happily ready to nourish ourselves with a homemade meal.

IT'S ALL ENERGY

Traditional Chinese medicine and the tradition of Macrobiotics view each food we eat, as well as the method in which it is prepared, as containing a particular energy. As we partake in the preparation and then take these foods into ourselves, we likewise take on those energies.[23] While these concepts are foreign to us here in the United States, they are actually pretty easy to understand.

For instance, close your eyes for a moment and take a deep breath. Tune into the quality of your breathing, the level of activity in your mind, the weight or buoyancy in your belly. Take note of how you feel, not just on a strictly physical level, but energetically. If there were a Vitality-Meter embedded into your forehead, where would the needle be? Drooping, hardly budging from the bottom of the spectrum? Pressing fervently against the far end of Fully Alive? Or perhaps floating somewhere in the middle?

We could also take a moment to visualize the Yin Yang symbol so familiar to many of us, with its curvaceously balanced black and white halves. This symbol represents the two sides of nature, to which we inextricably belong and cannot be separated. Yin is feminine, soft and receptive, while Yang is masculine, firm and aggressive. As with nature itself represented by the weather or a beautiful flowering cherry blossom tree, we must balance out these two halves within ourselves to feel a sense of equilibrium in our lives. Without its deep roots and sturdy branches, that exquisite Cherry Blossom could have no soft, green, curling leaves or delicately fluffy pink petals.

All these musings are presented here to bring awareness of the energy we carry at any particular time to the forefront of our attention. By tuning in, we have the ability and insight to then make choices that will assist us in bringing balance to our current state of being. For instance, say you wake slowly in the morning, a leaden quality to your eyelids. As you rise and begin to move about your day, your limbs protest, your bowels resist movement, and you feel as though a grey blanket of fog is resting, resiliently, over the surface of your brain. Not a super enticing morning description! And probably more familiar to most of us than we would like...

This is a perfect opportunity for the practice of food energetics. Rather than reaching for heavier, grounding foods such as meats, cheeses, grains or root vegetables, you could opt instead for lighter, uplifting foods such as leafy greens, crunchy veggies and fruits.

Besides the energy of the foods themselves, there is also the method in which we prepare our nourishment. Eating a raw salad will feed you differently than a plate of roasted or sautéed vegetables. Methods such as stewing, pressure cooking and baking produce a heavier, more grounding energy, where as boiling, steaming or eating our foods raw contains a much lighter, flexible energy.[23] While this information may at first seem like a foreign concept, it may become more intuitive. Consider how the vegetable grows to contemplate its energetic qualities. Carrots and parsnips are root vegetables that thrive in summer and autumn months and grow underneath the soil. Therefore, we can deduce that they will be warming to consume and offer us a grounded, rooted energy. A head of lettuce or stalk of celery, on the other hand, are full of water, vibrantly green, and grow upwards toward the sun. We can likewise deduce that these foods will offer us an increase in our energy, perhaps assisting us in feeling lighter, more optimistic and perhaps more creative. Where the foliage of a carrot collects energy from the sun and channels it downwards, the leaves of the lettuce directly absorb the photons radiating downward from on high, while its root system is simultaneously pulling nutrients upward. Both these veggies are incredibly healthy and beneficial to include in our diet, but when and how we consume them is one substantial way to bring energy where we need it most from day to day.

The process of eating according to food energetics allows us to grow more intimate with the foods we eat and how we prepare them, which in turn brings us closer to our mother earth as well as our own beautifully unique body. As with dietary doctrine in general, the most important aspect of this modality is to remain curious, to approach our diet with a beginner's mind. The more unattached I am to what I think is good for me, and the more receptive I can be to what my body requires today, the better I feel! Which, by the way, if you missed it somehow, is the point of all this.

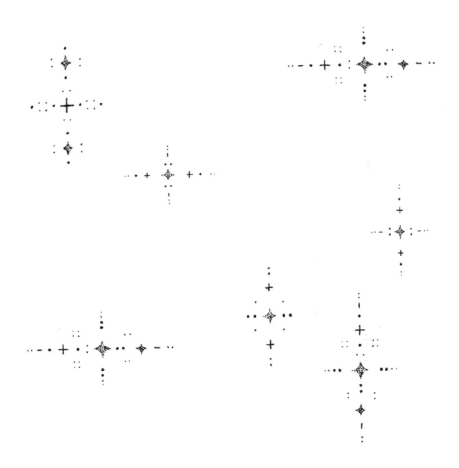

CHAPTER 7
TUNING IN

THE GRIP OF OUR VICES

As we move into making healthier choices on our plate, we are no doubt confronted by our old comforts and habits. While most of us know inherently that substances like alcohol and tobacco are addictive, we often do not think twice about sugar or caffeine. In truth, we take in these two speedy substances without pausing to consider if we really need them. It could be argued that America runs on coffee just as much as it runs on oil. If the coffee supply withered away tomorrow, the entire country's work force would fall face first onto their desks or workbench in a fatigue-induced coma.

And sugar, oh my... All those parents out there claiming their child is a "picky eater" may not realize that what they are really dealing with is a small human being whose taste buds are tainted by early overexposure to artificial sweetness. True, sugar is naturally occurring. However, it is only in our recent history that we have the liberty to eat it whenever we please. The sugarcane plant is a tropical species, and long ago, before the era of food transportation, humans only got to enjoy it on a very seldom basis. Even fruit, a category of foods that we completely take for granted as a staple of our daily diet, was not available to us as we now consume it. How many bananas per week do you eat? Now, where do you live? Unless you answered Hawaii or another tropical climate, that banana is a foreign substance introduced into the daily grind and incorporated as a basic item. We were never meant to eat these sugary, sweet foods as often as we do, and with absolute certainty, we are paying a high price. To see the rapid rise in obesity and diabetes as anything other than a nationwide sugar addiction is to live blindfolded.[24]

Both sugar and caffeine contribute to a host of ill health symptoms. In moderation of course, neither are problematic. Let us not live in denial though. Can you go to work or school without a cup of coffee? Can you make it through one day, functioning with sharp focus and a lively spirit, without that rather unholy sacrament? Can you go to bed without feeding a nagging sweet tooth? Do you notice constant cravings for sugar and sweet foods throughout your day?

Let me be clear: these questions are not meant to shame or guilt trip you into cooperation. I offer them purely as a wake-up call. So many of us go to yoga class, sit for meditation, and converse with our friends on the ideal of world peace, yet there is a hamster wheel of addiction humming in the background. I invite you to honestly examine your relationships with the foods and beverages you consume. No judgment here, to beat ourselves up does not help the situation. How do you feed yourself? And how is that playing out in your life? If you consider yourself a spiritual seeker, be bold and bring your attention not only to your breath, but to your habits. Because something is common does not make it wise. I believe one of our greatest tasks as a spiritual being in a human body is to loosen our grip on our attachments. And one of the very best ways to do this is with our addictions.

If this concept resonates somewhere in your psyche, know that there are alternatives! We can live without sugar cravings, enjoying fruits and processed sugars in moderation and delighting in naturally sweet foods such as carrots, squash and beets. We can live without the constant caffeine rush and inevitable crash, opting instead for nurturing herbs, a full night's sleep and drinking plenty of good ol' fashioned pure water. I used to be a daily coffee drinker. I love the taste, I love the ritual... I get it, people. I have now been off regular caffeine usage for 4 years and counting, and I can honestly report I have more energy than ever. Imagine waking up from a delicious slumber and feeling rested, enthusiastic and ready to step into the day with a glass of water or cup of herbal tea in hand. It is possible! And now, I can enjoy a cup of coffee or Earl Grey from time to time without attachment, simply delighting in the gift of its beneficial properties without the grip of necessity.

OFF THE PLATE

There is a myth telling us if we just eat enough green stuff, if we can just consume enough veggies, if we can just burn more calories than we take in, if we can just find that perfect diet and get our body under control, then we will finally be healthy. In truth, many are the facets to the gem of good health. What we eat is one of them, and while it is certainly an important factor, it is only one of many. We are also told that we are what we eat. I have already suggested that we are also how we eat. So the question is, how do you feed yourself? How do you nourish your body, mind, heart? Thankfully, we are so much more than this human body, and how we feel hinges not only upon our nutrient and vitamin intake, but also the thoughts, feelings and beliefs we digest constantly.

This concept can be explained further with the idea of Primary and Secondary Food™₂₅. Secondary Food is the stuff we eat, everything on our plate that we physically digest. Primary Food is everything that feeds us off our plate— the rest of our life! Namely, our spirituality, relationships, work, and exercise. These areas, referred to by the Institute for Integrative Nutrition® as Primary Food, have been referenced here in this section and have profoundly affected the way I coach others and myself into a more holistically healthy life.

How is your marriage or partnership? How is your love life, your level of intimacy, your ability to be vulnerable? How are your friendships? Do you seek and desire partnership but feel as though you are falling short of attracting your ideal mate? Are you unsatisfied with your current relationship? How much do you actually like the people you surround yourself with? These questions may seem like obvious indicators of our quality of life, but it is amazing how much focus we give to our physical health, while ignoring the state of our heart and how we feel about our role in a community.

Do you love your career? Do you despise your career? Or perhaps you are somewhere in between, resigned and repeating a weekly habit of showing up for a vocation that once moved you but now solely represents a paycheck... Do you dream of being more engaged, perhaps working from home, but feel completely stuck in the reliability of steady income?

How do you move your body? Have you discovered a form of exercise that speaks to you, that excites you and motivates you to pull on your sneakers after an 8-hour work day or get up an hour early? Or perhaps intentionally bringing yourself to a sweat is like pulling teeth, something you loathe and take great pains to avoid...

How about your spiritual life? Is there such a thing? Do you have a regular practice of which you are a disciple? Do you show up for yourself and your spirit? Do you feel a compelling sense to dive deeper into your essence and truth, to know yourself and contemplate the mysteries of your life? Do these areas possess more or less importance than what you eat? And looking among them, do you find certain topics that feel dire and valuable, while others you easily shrug off?

These questions represent how we nourish ourselves in a holistic sense, and I am here to argue that they are just as important, if not more so, than the amount of leafy greens we consume. In addition, they are all interconnected. It is not a secret that how we eat and which foods we are drawn to have been shaped by our past. The same could be said for how we move our bodies, the quality of our relationships, the level of satisfaction we feel with our vocation, and finally our relationship with divinity, however that word translates for you.

Awareness changes everything. This entire book is an invitation to mindfulness and attentive self-care. I adore witnessing my clients make connections between the neighboring regions of wellness in their lives. It is not a small thing to realize one seemingly isolated habit is contributing to an entire system of disfunction. Just as looking at one body part while neglecting the whole represents a broken medical system, a single-pointed approach to a healthy dietary regimen neglects the holistic nature of the human being. Made of cells, organs and bones, we are also made of mood, belief and attachment. Peace is a crucial ingredient in the secret sauce, as is joy.

Where is the bitterness in your life? You could add cane sugar to your tea or, perhaps, a book of Rumi poetry, a weekly walk with a beloved, or a change in your career might accomplish the same desired effect.

We often look to our food to fill gaping holes created by our lifestyles, with a result of emotional eating, obesity, candida or addiction. Where in your life are you starving? What is the flavor of your perpetual hunger? Look beyond the obvious for ideas and answers. Seek recipes to make your heart salivate and serve deep satiety to your soul. This is the way to true health, my friends. You need not, and in fact you cannot, do it alone. As mythologist Joseph Campbell sagely advised, "Follow your bliss and the universe will open doors for you where there were only walls."

FOLLOW YOUR GUT

Hippocrates, often cited as the grandfather of medicine, is famously quoted as saying *"Let food be thy medicine and medicine be thy food."* This ancient Greek physician was spot on, and his humble suggestion brings up a deep truth, seeded in the richly diverse soil of individuality.

We've all heard the saying *to each their own.* And yet, we all seem to flock to the same popular diet book, or sign up for the newest exercise fitness fad at the gym, or subscribe to the questionable rationale that there is a "healthy" way to eat across all borders. The truth?

We all require an exclusive prescription.

By prescription, I mean how many hours we sleep, whether we are a vegan, vegetarian or omnivore, what percentage of each meals is raw. I mean what we do to move our bodies and how we express our emotions and expel our aggressions. I mean how we flex our creativity, how we exercise our mind, how we find peace. I mean the introverted or extroverted nature of our social tendencies and how we best learn new information. All of our self-care, in its rainbow variety of forms, colors, shapes and sizes, comes together to write a prescription exclusive to you and you alone. But here is the catch: what if this prescription is only relevant for one day? What if tomorrow, you had to write yourself a new one?

This suggestion lies at the beating, brilliant heart of what it means to be truly healthy.

No one way of eating (or living, for that matter) will ever work for everyone. Each of us is changing constantly. From moment to moment, our cells are literally shifting, shedding, dying, repairing, and renewing. From day to day, we jump from one scenario to the next, preparing a fresh, home-cooked mountain of steamed greens from our garden on

Monday night and eating Danish pancakes slathered in whipped cream and topped with cinnamon sprinkled apples on Saturday morning.

> **Our body responds to differing nutrients and environments exactly as it needs to in order to keep functioning, and the way we feel is our indicator of how well we are matching what we put into our body with what our body actually wants to be fed.**

All too often, I witness people all around me subscribing to what others are doing, what they are told is the right thing to do or eat or drink, rather than tuning in and having that most sacred and sensitive of conversations with their own gut. If we could still ourselves before each meal, before we walk into that restaurant or enter a friend's home, and simply ask ourselves, *what do you need to be fed in order to thrive?* and wait for the response, and then actually follow through on that request, how different would our lives be? How different would our bodies look and feel? It has become a part of my practice to constantly question my own behaviors when it comes to feeding myself. I would call myself an omnivore, yet I go through phases where I hardly eat any meat for months at a time. When we attach ourselves to a doctrine, we become rigid and unyielding rather than remaining flexible to the shifting needs of our human form. What works for me today may not work for me tomorrow. A green smoothie is my perfect breakfast in the summertime, but when winter comes I am much more drawn to a hot bowl of quinoa porridge. Only you can unravel the truth of how you feel when you eat fruit for breakfast, or if caffeine really serves you, or if fermented foods assist with your digestion, or if you really can tolerate gluten.

From day to day, week to week, month to month, season to season, year to year, decade to decade, we are a work in progress; an ever-evolving canvas begging for wild new colors and intriguingly unfamiliar textures in order to represent the current state of our inner and outer landscape. The key to unlocking our highest potential is allowing ourselves to change, embracing those transmutations as they occur, and welcoming new habits to form or old ones to fall away. By doing this, we can step forth and heed the call of our deepest and authentically personal needs.

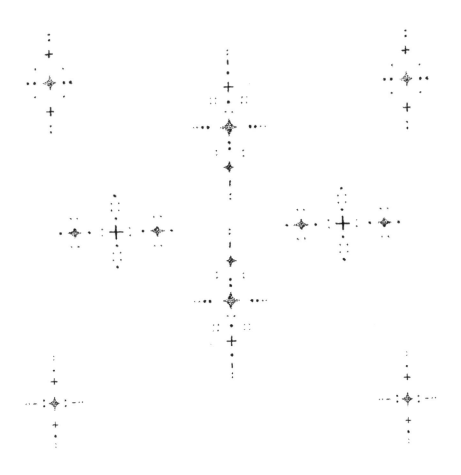

CHAPTER 8
MIRACULOUS MEDICINE

WHY IT MATTERS

Each grey green leaf on a eucalyptus tree exists because of the elements and nutrients which birthed it. There are no accidents here. The soil collects molecular compounds and absorbs all its essential nourishment, sucking it up like a straw through each branching limb of its subterranean root system. The sun shining from above excites chlorophyll, which makes sugars that feed the plant. Each peeling layer of bark, each new sprouting arm, is there by the grace of the nutrients fed to the tree by the breast of mother earth herself. Our bodies are the very same. Infinitely complex and endlessly wise, they take what they need from the nourishment we offer. They absorb nutrients in exactly the right quantities and dosage, parceling those ingredients out to the appropriate bodily system so that we can thrive. All the while, we excrete waste and discard toxins that do not serve or threaten the whole by way of our sweat, urine, feces and saliva. Brilliant you are! And yet, just as a tree will become diseased and rot from the inside when assaulted by destructive critters or threatening bacteria, or when parched of its necessary nourishment, we witness signs on a daily basis of imbalance in our own body.

What is insane is that when we see such signals of dis-ease, we have been taught to first, seek outside ourselves for initial and resounding judgment on the reason for the imbalance, and second, address the symptom of imbalance with a chemically constructed pill, created specifically to remove all signs of the symptom itself without addressing the reason for its existence in the first place.

Which, of course, in no way prevents the symptom from returning at a later date for the exact same reason it initially appeared. If you have an ant problem in your kitchen, it is probably not wise to leave out a plate of sugar-sweetened chocolate chunk cookies on your counter. Nor is it logical to simply sweep the thick marching sentinel of tiny insects off your counter, wipe your hands and walk away thinking you have solved the problem.

As ridiculous as this sounds, it's an accurate metaphor to describe our systematic solution to illness in America. Does it work? Absolutely not. It does not take a scientist to plainly deduce that our healthcare system is really a disease-care system. More than two in three adults are considered to be overweight or obese.[26] More than two out of three! Can we just sit with that for a moment? Add about one-third of children and adolescents 6-19 years old to that list, and the number of unhealthy people in our country begins to bring on serious nausea. If that isn't awful enough, cancer is now the second most common cause of death in the United States, trailing behind heart disease. Over 1.5 million new cases of cancer will have been diagnosed in 2016 alone, and about 1,630 people are estimated to die from cancer every day in this country.[27] Then you have cardiovascular disease, which takes the cake as the number one killer of Americans.

Yes, this is a total downer. It is also our reality. For all the money we pour into healthcare (over 3.5 trillion dollars in 2016), we maintain the lowest life expectancy and poorest overall health conditions compared to a dozen other high-income nations.[28] Not only is this downright pathetic, it is literally tragic. And while I can (and have) let this information sweep me into a corner, cowering and shaking in helpless misery, instead I am choosing to take action. Some will choose to protest. Others will start movements. Activism is a broad and colorful umbrella and we all have the freedom here in America, thank goodness, to choose our own path. You may not believe that the simple act of eating clean and devoting yourself to a life of holistic nourishment is much of a radical statement. I beg to differ.

If you and one hundred of your friends and acquaintances adopted the practices offered in this book, I believe you would soon see major shifts in your local community. If each one of those folks had one hundred people begin to adopt these practices, I believe we would begin to see major shifts on a national and eventually, a global level. Feeling good is infectious. When I say feeling good, I mean feeling joyful, looking radiant, skin luminous, belly happy, heart healthy, toes to crown fully nurtured and feeling vibrant from the inside, out. Do you have a friend like that? Someone in your life who is just a beauteous example of a human being? (Hopefully you have at least one!) Of course, they are not perfect. They have lovely flaws and an ego with which they are likely grappling, like all of us. But overall, they magnetize others around them because they beam out a steady stream of positive, healthy, balanced, thriving vibrations. They are an inspiration to all those around them, whether they know it or not. This could be you. Let this be you!

Why does it matter? It matters because the quality of your life depends upon it! What we eat and how we eat it, how we feed ourselves, is everything. How we show up in the world; for our job on Mondays, for our lover under the sheets, for our parents on their birthdays, for ourselves when we become stressed out; all these things are reflections of the nourishment we provide ourselves. And in turn, we recycle that nourishment, or lack thereof, feeding those in our immediate circles constant doses of either vitality or venom. Not only is our body immediately affected by the foods we ingest and the ways we ingest them, but so is our energy, our mood, our libido, our quality of breath. Our life force. We move about our home, our neighborhood and our communities, dosing our surroundings as we go.

Why does it matter? Because we can change the quality of our lives with the choices we make! And because it is not just about us. When we get cancer, our community suffers. My parents have reached the age where their friends have begun to die. They are only entering their 70s. Cancer seems to be all around them, and I watch them mourn the increasingly steady stream of chemo patients, fervently praying for their own health and for the health of my own generation. What will become of us, the millennials? What will it take for us to wake up and step up to the responsibility of being a human being on planet earth right now?

Albert Einstein said, "There are only two ways to live your life. One is as though nothing is a miracle. The other is as though everything is a miracle." If we choose the latter, then being alive in this age is a thrilling opportunity. The miracle of the mess is our ability to clean it up and, in the process, our opportunity to learn what created it in the first place.

COMMON VS. NORMAL

Way too often we confuse these two words. They are very pertinent to health issues and I suggest we call it like it is. Gas, bloating, and constipation are NOT normal. No matter how long we have suffered from these symptoms, the truth is that the body produces these effects to cope with an imbalance taking place. I have friends who have defended their nearly constant farting, protesting, "this is just normal for me! Is it possible that this is just how my body is?"

No. No, it is not possible.

And for the record, my ears start ringing on high alert whenever I hear the phrase *this is just how it is*, or *this is just how I am*.

Allow these combinations of words to set off an alarm bell in your head, for that is the cue that we have slid into a dangerous comfort zone by accepting our circumstances without questioning whether it is changeable or desirable. By all means, question your ailments! Get curious. Seek the truth. Empower yourself by becoming a food sleuth. There are many ways to take on the role of a food detective, and the best place to start is with ourselves. Elimination diets, cleanses, detoxes and food allergy tests are all wondrous labyrinths where we can discover any number of surprisingly disruptive eating habits we've had for years or even our entire lifetime.

This past summer I went on a three-month elimination diet, more out of curiosity than to address any specific symptom, but I did long to discover the cause of my frequent headaches and eliminate them from my life. During those three months, I continued to suffer from occasional headaches, and though I suspected that perhaps a certain amount of detoxifying was taking place, I felt rather defeated that they did not vanish. Fast forward to the present day. It has been more than eight months since my elimination diet ended, and I have stopped eating gluten, corn, yeast, almonds and cashews. (Visit the *Tales from the Trenches* chapter for the gruesome details.) One day several months after the diet concluded, I had a startling realization that literally stopped me mid-sentence. I could not remember the last time I had a headache. Wide-eyed and incredulous, I scanned my memory for any possible occurrence I had missed, for any logical explanation. I arrived back at the diet, at the short but potent list of foods I had eliminated and now been free of for six months. It is almost impossible to believe, because I have identified with being a person who just gets headaches for as long as I can remember. I thought it was normal. I figured it might be a chemical imbalance in my brain that would never equalize, and that I would just need to suck it up and deal with it, till death do us part.

For now, I am overjoyed to say, what appeared to be *normal* turned out to be a symptom.

FOOD FIRST

Tom Malterre, author of <u>The Elimination Diet</u>, suggests that food itself is our primary nutrient, which also makes it our primary irritant. The deeper into the nutritional jungle I wander, the more certain I become that food is a portal into understanding the secret of life. How much we can learn from a simple raspberry, from the miraculous array of elements that created it, and the way in which we first eat it, then digest, absorb and utilize its magic. When I give thanks before a meal, I never stick to saying any one thing in particular, but I do often come around to somehow expressing gratitude for the divinity apparent in the digestion of our food.

We take in the fruits of god, be it a lettuce leaf, blueberry, grain of quinoa or slice of aged sharp cheddar, and somehow, we contain the innate wisdom to savor each morsel on our tongue, integrate the nutrients into our own body, expel the remnants and then go out into the world and serve, fueled by our nourishment.

Hippocrates' quote is so deliciously satisfying to my soul that I will serve it up for you here once more.

"Let food be thy medicine, and thy medicine be food."

I have plainly suggested here in this collection of words, phrases and ideas that we heed this advice. But I want to clarify what I mean by medicine.

Let food soothe your ailments. Let it address your illnesses. Let it be the first suspect when you are unwell, and the first balm to nurse you back to health. Let it be examined, monitored, experimented with and tested, repeatedly. Let it be celebrated. Let it be used in careful moderation, with consideration for its potency and full ingredient list. Let it be honored and exalted. Let it be taken with gratitude, accepted with grace, and eaten with devotion.

Medicine also speaks to our personal power. The native indigenous cultures of the world used the word "medicine" to describe an individual's strengths, their personal medicine being the gift they bring to the community, the place they hold, the role they take on. Each of us carries our own unique medicine, a perfectly concocted combination of strengths, skills, and abilities that gives us our charm and our knowing of where we can best give back to our world.

Let us factor food into our personal medicine. How we treat our plant and animal relations, how we treat one another, and how we treat ourselves displays a plainly honest portrait of how we show up in the world. Our spirit flavors everything we do. It is the iridescent thread holding our physical lives and our energetic presence together. We are inseparable from it, and therefore all we do is bound up in a beautiful prayer bundle of rosemary, dried sage, lavender blossoms and thyme leaves, ready to be dropped with love into your next pot of vegetable stew. Each step of the journey is a bite. Chew slowly and delight in the savory sweet delicacies of your life. I believe we are here in these bodies to experience the contrast of light and dark, and then choose joy, savoring each morsel of the present moment as if it were our last.

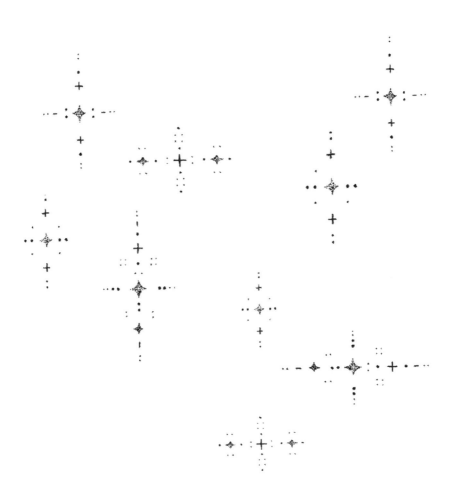

HERE TO HELP

With a foundation in holistic, heart-based nourishment, I assist my clients to align body and spirit. An Integrative Nutrition Health Coach, certified yoga teacher and essential oil educator, my path is rooted in the wonderment of nature and the wisdom of our physical bodies.

Also a musician & dancer, I believe wholeheartedly in the power of sound, movement, and stillness, and weave this potent medicine into all my offerings.

Working with clients to achieve their aspirations of personal transformation, my goal is to empower and guide others towards an embodied lifestyle of joy and fulfillment, grounded in daily practices that feed us on all levels.

I offer free Discovery Sessions for anyone curious and intrigued by the idea of working with me. I would delight in spending one hour with you where you get to talk about all the most important things happening in your life, I get to listen with my heart wide open, and together we will hone in on the areas of your life needing extra love and find some creative approaches to your unique version of "healthy."

I serve up a variety of delectable services, including 6-month and 1-month intensive programs for individuals and groups, and I am available to work in person in Santa Barbara and Los Angeles, or globally via Skype or telephone.

IIN

I am a graduate and certified health coach of the **Institute for Integrative Nutrition**® **(IIN)**, whose teachings are widely distributed in this book and in the mentorship and guidance of health practitioners around the globe.

IIN offers a truly comprehensive Health Coach Training Program that invites students to deeply explore the things that are most nourishing to them. From the physical aspects of nutrition and eating wholesome foods that work best for each individual person, to the concept of Primary Food – the idea that everything in life, including our spirituality, career, relationships, and fitness contributes to our inner and outer health – IIN helped me reach optimal health and balance. This inner journey unleashed the passion that compels me to share what I've learned and inspire others.

Beyond personal health, IIN offers training in health coaching, as well as business and marketing. Students who choose to pursue this field professionally complete the program equipped with the communication skills and branding knowledge they need to create a fulfilling career encouraging and supporting others in reaching their own health goals.

From renowned wellness experts as Visiting Teachers to the convenience of their online learning platform, my experience at this school has changed my life. If you are called to this work, I invite you to learn more about the Institute for Integrative Nutrition and explore how the Health Coach Training Program can help you transform your life. For more information on their extensive curriculum and holistic concepts, to learn more about working with me, or to start a conversation about becoming a health coach yourself, feel free to contact me at www.brittagreenviolet.com/integrativenutrition, or call (844) 315-8546 to learn more.

REFERENCES

This book was lovingly written utilizing both my personal experience roaming and exploring the wide wilderness of holistic nourishment, as well as many external resources, references and inspirations. Below is a breakdown, chapter by chapter, of references made in this text.

Preface

Introductions

Frost, R. (2007). *Stopping by woods on a snowy evening*. Belleville, IL: Two Sisters Press.

Courted by curiosity

Clear, J. (2014, April 10). How Long Does It Actually Take to Form a New Habit? (Backed by Science). Retrieved March 07, 2017, from http://www.huffingtonpost.com/james-clear/forming-new-habits_b_5104807.html

Selk, J. (n.d.). Habit Formation: The 21-Day Myth. Retrieved March 08, 2017, from https://www.forbes.com/forbes/welcome/?toURL=https%3A%2F%2Fwww.forbes.com%2Fsites%2Fjasonselk%2F2013%2F04%2F15%2Fhabit-formation-the-21-day-myth%2F&refURL=&referrer=#2a5c71746fed

Chapter 1: Eating, A Spiritual Frontier

On the word "practice"

Practice. (n.d.). Retrieved March 08, 2017, from https://www.merriam-webster.com/dictionary/practice

Vote with your spoon

In Defense of Food. (n.d.). Retrieved March 08, 2017, from

http://michaelpollan.com/books/in-defense-of-food/

DeNoon, D. J. (2009, March 23). 7 Rules for Eating. Retrieved March 08, 2017,

from http://www.webmd.com/food-recipes/news/20090323/7-rules-for-eating#1

Chapter 2: A Little Taste

Creating Sacred Space

Hanh, T. N. (2014). *How to eat*. Place of Berkeley, CA: Parallax Pr.

Three Breaths

Douillard, J. (2015, July 28). 15 Benefits of Nose Breathing Exercise | John

Douillard's Lifespa. Retrieved March 08, 2017, from http://lifespa.com/15-benefits-

nose-breathing-exercise

Allen, J. (2013, August 16). Mouth Breathing Vs. Nasal Breathing. Retrieved March 08, 2017, from http://www.livestrong.com/article/255298-mouth-breathing-vs-nasal-breathing/

Winick, D. R. (2015, May 06). Why You Should Practice Breathing Through Your Nose (And Not Your Mouth). Retrieved March 08, 2017, from http://www.mindbodygreen.com/0-18512/why-you-should-practice-breathing-through-your-nose-and-not-your-mouth.html

Lawrence, G. (n.d.). Breathing Is Believing: The Importance of Nasal Breathing. Retrieved March 08, 2017, from http://www.gaiam.com/discover/670/article/breathing-believing-importance-nasal-breathing/

Chapter 3: Digging In

Habit of hydration

Sugar 101. (n.d.). Retrieved March 23, 2017, from http://www.heart.org/HEARTORG/HealthyLiving/HealthyEating/Nutrition/Sugar-101_UCM_306024_Article.jsp#.WM_6KhLyvfA

Hughes, L. (2016, June 06). Here's How Much Sugar You're Really Eating in a Day. Retrieved March 23, 2017, from http://greatist.com/eat/how-much-sugar-per-day

Mastication Meditation

Danahy, A. (2015, April 26). What Are the Digestive Enzymes in the Stomach & Mouth Called? Retrieved March 23, 2017, from http://www.livestrong.com/article/423200-what-are-the-digestive-enzymes-in-the-stomach-mouth-called/

Mercola, D. (n.d.). 7 Important Reasons to Properly Chew Your Food. Retrieved March 08, 2017, from http://www.quantumhealing.co.za/7-important-reasons-to-properly-chew-your-food.html

Leaky gut syndrome. (2017, March 08). Retrieved March 08, 2017, from https://en.wikipedia.org/wiki/Leaky_gut_syndrome

Axe, D. (2017, February 24). 4 Steps to Heal Leaky Gut and Autoimmune Disease. Retrieved March 08, 2017, from https://draxe.com/4-steps-to-heal-leaky-gut-and-autoimmune-disease/

Chapter 4: Easy Does It

Diet Vs. Lifestyle

Fad. (n.d.). Retrieved March 08, 2017, from http://www.dictionary.com/browse/fad

"Fall In Love With The Truth of Your Shape"

Arrien, A., Ph.D. (1993). *The four-fold way: walking the paths of the warrior, teacher, healer, and visionary* (1st ed.). San Francisco: HarperSanFrancisco.

Chapter 5: Earthly Delights

A Sustainable Kitchen

Ryan, S. (2015, October 25). The Easy Way To Tell Which Plastics Go In The Recycle Bin. Retrieved March 08, 2017, from http://greenopedia.com/plastic-recycling-codes/

Society, N. G. (2012, October 09). Great Pacific Garbage Patch. Retrieved March 08, 2017, from http://www.nationalgeographic.org/encyclopedia/great-pacific-garbage-patch/

Mama, K. -. (n.d.). The Problems with Plastic | Wellness Mama. Retrieved March 08, 2017, from https://wellnessmama.com/23757/dangers-of-plastic/

Learn About Glass. (n.d.). Retrieved March 08, 2017, from http://gpi.org/learn-about-glass

Woerner, A. (n.d.). What are natural flavors, really? Retrieved March 08, 2017, from http://www.cnn.com/2015/01/14/health/feat-natural-flavors-explained/

Smith, J. (n.d.). Retrieved March 08, 2017, from https://www.ted.com/talks/joe_smith_how_to_use_a_paper_towel

(n.d.). Retrieved March 08, 2017, from http://quoteinvestigator.com/2013/12/09/safe-harbor/

Chapter 6: The Whole Truth

Tales from the trenches

Malterre, T. (2016). *The elimination diet: discover the foods that are making you sick and tired--and feel better fast*(1st ed.). New York: Boston.

Food Energetics

Gagné, S. (2008). *Food energetics: the spiritual, emotional, and nutritional power of what we eat*. Rochester, VT: Healing Arts Press.

Chapter 7: Tuning In

The Grip of Our Vices

Gameau, D. (Director). (2014). *That Sugar Film*[Motion picture]. Australia: Madman Distributor / Samuel Goldwyn Films.

Soechtig, S. (Director). (2014). *Fed Up*[Motion picture]. United States of America: Atlas Films / RADiUS-TWC.

Off the Plate

"The Institute For Integrative Nutrition", "IIN" and "Primary Foods" are trademarks of Integrative Nutrition Inc®. The concepts of Bio-IINdividuality® and Primary Foods® are trademarks of The Institute of Integrative Nutrition®, and foundational aspects of their methodology. Those ideas are represented throughout this book, and specifically can be found, expressed in my own words, in the chapters "Follow Your Gut" and "Off the Plate", respectively.

Chapter 8: Miraculous Medicine

Why It Matters

Overweight and Obesity Statistics. (n.d.). Retrieved March 08, 2017, from https://www.niddk.nih.gov/health-information/health-statistics/pages/overweight-obesity-statistics.aspx

Cancer Facts & Figures 2017. (n.d.). Retrieved March 08, 2017, from https://www.cancer.org/research/cancer-facts-statistics/all-cancer-facts-figures/cancer-facts-figures-2017.html

National Health Expenditures 2015 Highlights . (2015). Retrieved March 8, 2017, from https://www.cms.gov/research-statistics-data-and-systems/statistics-trends-and-reports/nationalhealthexpenddata/downloads/highlights.pdf